Data Integrity and Compliance

A Primer for Medical Product Manufacturers

Also available from ASQ Quality Press:

Quality Experience Telemetry
Alka Jarvis, Luis Morales, Johnson Jose

Human Error Reduction in Manufacturing
José Rodríguez-Pérez

Quality Risk Management in the FDA-Regulated Industry, Second Edition
José Rodríguez-Pérez

Handbook of Investigation and Effective CAPA Systems, Second Edition
José Rodríguez-Pérez

The FDA and Worldwide Current Good Manufacturing Practices and Quality System Requirements Guidebook for Finished Pharmaceuticals
José Rodríguez-Pérez

The Certified Six Sigma Green Belt Handbook, Second Edition
Roderick A. Munro, Govindarajan Ramu, and Daniel J. Zrymiak

The ASQ Six Sigma Black Belt Pocket Guide
T.M. Kubiak

The Certified Six Sigma Black Belt Handbook, Third Edition
T.M. Kubiak and Donald W. Benbow

The Certified Six Sigma Yellow Belt Handbook
Govindarajan Ramu

The Quality Toolbox, Second Edition
Nancy R. Tague

The Certified Manager of Quality/Organizational Excellence Handbook, Fourth Edition
Russell T. Westcott, editor

To request a complimentary catalog of ASQ Quality Press publications, call 800-248-1946, or visit our website at http://www.asq.org/quality-press.

Data Integrity and Compliance

A Primer for Medical Product Manufacturers

José Rodríguez-Pérez, PhD

ASQ Quality Press
Milwaukee, Wisconsin

American Society for Quality, Quality Press, Milwaukee 53203
© 2019 by ASQ. Printed in 2019.
All rights reserved.
Printed in the United States of America.
22 21 20 19   5 4 3 2 1

Library of Congress Cataloging-in-Publication Data

Names: Rodríguez Pérez, José, 1961– author. | American Society for Quality, issuing body.
Title: Data integrity and compliance : a primer for medical product manufacturers /
    by Jose Rodriguez-Perez.
Description: Milwaukee, Wisconsin : ASQ Quality Press, [2019] | Includes bibliographical
    references and index.
Identifiers: LCCN 2019003748 | ISBN 9780873899871 (hardcover : alk. paper)
Subjects: | MESH: Pharmaceutical Preparations—standards | Computer Security—
    standards | Equipment and Supplies—standards | Quality Control | Drug Industry—
    standards | Data Accuracy | United States
Classification: LCC RS122.2 | NLM QV 771 | DDC 615.10285—dc23 LC record available
    at https://lccn.loc.gov/2019003748

Publisher: Seiche Sanders
Sr. Creative Services Specialist: Randy L. Benson

ASQ Mission: The American Society for Quality advances individual, organizational, and
community excellence worldwide through learning, quality improvement, and knowledge
exchange.

Attention Bookstores, Wholesalers, Schools, and Corporations: ASQ Quality Press books,
video, audio, and software are available at quantity discounts with bulk purchases for
business, educational, or instructional use. For information, please contact ASQ Quality
Press at 800-248-1946, or write to ASQ Quality Press, P.O. Box 3005, Milwaukee, WI
53201–3005.

To place orders or to request a free copy of the ASQ Quality Press Publications Catalog,
visit our website at http://www.asq.org/quality-press.

 Printed on acid-free paper.

Quality Press
600 N. Plankinton Ave.
Milwaukee, WI 53203-2914
E-mail: authors@asq.org

The Global Voice of Quality®

This book is dedicated to my parents.

In loving memory of my mother, Josefa, who is no longer with us but whose love and guidance are such a big part of me.

And to my father, Ginés, for your endurance and perseverance.

The work ethics and strength both of you taught me are my guide today.

Table of Contents

List of Tables

Acronyms

AIP	Application Integrity Policy
ALCOA	Attributable, Legible, Contemporaneous, Original, and Accurate
ANDA	Abbreviated New Drug Application
API	Active Pharmaceutical Ingredient
CFR	Code of Federal Regulations
CDER	Center for Drug Evaluation and Research
CMC	Chemistry, Manufacturing, and Controls
CoA	Certificates of Analysis
CRF	Case Report Form
CRO	Contract Research Organization
DMF	Drug Master File
DQ	Design Qualification
EBR	Electronic Batch Record
ECG	Electrocardiogram
eCRF	Electronic Case Report Form
EMA	European Medicines Agency
FAT	Factory Acceptance Testing
FDA	Food and Drug Administration
FDASIA	Food and Drug Administration Safety and Innovation Act
FD&C	Food, Drug, and Cosmetic Act
FT-IR	Fourier-Transform Infrared Spectroscopy
GC	Gas Chromatograph
GCP	Good Clinical Practice
GDEA	Generic Drug Enforcement Act
GDP	Good Distribution Practice
GDocP	Good Documentation Practice
GLP	Good Laboratory Practice

GMP	Good Manufacturing Practice, also cited as cGMP (Current Good Manufacturing Practice)
GXP	Good Practice
HPLC	High-Performance Liquid Chromatography
ICH	International Conference on Harmonization
IQ	Installation Qualification
IRB	Institutional Review Board
ISO	International Standardization Organization
IT	Information Technology
LIMS	Laboratory Information Management System
MHRA	Medicines and Healthcare Products Regulatory Agency
OOS	Out of Specification
OQ	Operational Qualification
ORA	Office of Regulatory Affairs
PAI	Preapproval Inspection
PDF	Portable Document Format
PIC/S	Pharmaceutical Inspection Co-operation Scheme
PLC	Programmable Logic Controller
PQ	Performance Qualification
QA	Quality Assurance
QC	Quality Control
QMS	Quality Management System
QRM	Quality Risk Management
SAT	Site Acceptance Testing
SOP	Standard Operating Procedure
URS	User Requirement Specification
USP	United States Pharmacopeia
UV/Vis	Ultraviolet/Visible Spectrophotometry
WHO	World Health Organization

Preface

In recent years, there has been a dramatic increase in the number of U.S. Food and Drug Administration (FDA) warning letters, World Health Organization (WHO) notices of concern, and European Medicines Agency (EMA) statements of noncompliance in which false or misleading information has been identified during regulatory inspections. Failure to properly manage data integrity in regulated healthcare industries applies equally to paper and electronic data. It can arise either from poor systematic control of the data management systems due to a lack of knowledge, careless work, or intentionally hidden, falsified, or misleading data. This is troubling because ensuring data integrity is a critical component of the industry's responsibility to ensure the safety, efficacy, and quality of medical products, and of regulators' ability to protect the public health. In the case of the U.S. FDA, these data integrity–related current good manufacturing practice (cGMP) violations have led to numerous regulatory actions, including warning letters, import alerts, and consent decrees.

In the medical product manufacturing field, data integrity lapses are not limited to fraud or falsification. They can be totally unintentional and still pose risk. Therefore, any potential for compromising the reliability of data is a risk that must be identified and understood in order to place appropriate controls to manage them.

Data integrity is a global mandatory requirement for the regulated healthcare industry. It is more than a mere expectation. It is also a basic element of good documentation practices, one of the most fundamental pillars of quality management systems (QMSs), including cGMP. Developing and bringing a medical product to market involves different players and activities; therefore, robustness and accuracy of the data submitted by manufacturers to regulatory authorities is crucial. The data must be comprehensive, complete, accurate, and true to ensure the quality of studies supporting applications for medical products to be placed on the market.

The purpose of this book is to consolidate existing principles and expectations from several regulatory sources into a single and handy document providing detailed illustrative implementation guidance. It must be considered as a means of understanding comprehensive regulatory agencies' position on good data management/data integrity and the minimum expectation on how medical product's manufacturers can achieve compliance.

Sources of principles and expectations for data integrity used in this book were the following: EMA *Questions and Answers: Good Manufacturing Practice-Data Integrity* (2016), WHO *Guidance on Good Data Management and Record Management Practices* (2016), U.S. FDA *Guidance for Industry on Data Integrity and Compliance with cGMP* (2018), Pharmaceutical Inspection Co-operation Scheme (PIC/S) Draft *Guidance Good Practices for Data Management and Integrity in Regulated GMP/GDP Environments* (2018), and the UK Medicines and Healthcare Products Regulatory Agency (MHRA) *GXP Data Integrity Definitions and Guidance* (2018).

I would like to acknowledge the tremendous job performed by authors and reviewers from above-mentioned FDA, EMA, MHRA, PIC/S, and WHO guidance documents. All of you are doing a terrific job developing meaningful expectations and requirements that contributes to the availability of safer medical products.

Although above-mentioned guidance documents used the word "should" (as they contain mostly nonbinding recommendations rather than regulations) when referring to good data management and data integrity expectations, I used the much stronger word "must" to denote the obligation to perform such activity in order to establish effective data management controls and to avoid problems during regulatory inspections.

Regulatory expectations are that all data be reliable and accurate and good data management practices apply to all elements of the medical product manufacturing quality systems. Table 4.1 depicts the U.S. FDA § 21 Code of Federal Regulations (CFR) part 211cGMP requirements for attributable, legible, contemporaneous, original, and accurate (ALCOA) data. While some of the requirements are fully explicit (for example, § 211.110 or § 211.160 requirements for contemporaneous recording of data), others are more implicit. But all of them are requirements. Table 4.2 includes similar EU EudraLex Volume 4 cGMP requirements.

This book focuses on the application of data management principles and procedures to the manufacturing of medical products, covering the whole supply chain, from suppliers of raw materials and components to the distribution of finished products and pharmacovigilance activities. The focus is on those principles that are implicit in existing guidance documents and regulations and that, if not robustly implemented, can impact reliability and completeness of data and undermine the robustness of decision making based upon those data. Illustrative examples are provided as to how these principles may be applied to current situations. Additionally, it gives explanations as to what these high-level requirements mean in practice and what must be demonstrably implemented to achieve compliance.

The scope of this book is designated as "GXP" in that everything contained here is good practice (GXP) unless stated otherwise. The same good documentation practices (GDocPs) apply to manufacturing (GMP), clinical (GCP), laboratory (GLP), distribution (GDP), pharmacovigilance, and so on.

The recommendations contained in this book apply equally to all type of data (paper, electronic, hybrid, and so on) and to all type of regulated products (pharmaceutical, medical devices, veterinary, cosmetics, food, and dietary supplements). All of them must abide by the same rules regarding completeness, consistency, and accuracy of data. Other activities such as clinical trials must also adhere to those rules.

This book aims to promote a risk-based approach to data management that includes data risk, criticality, and life cycle. Readers of this book need to understand their data processes (as a life cycle) to identify data with the greatest GXP impact. From that, the identification of the most effective and efficient risk-based control and review of the data can be determined and implemented.

The introductory content of Chapter 1 presents the basic principles and expectation of good documentation practices and data integrity, including definitions of key terms and the introduction to the ALCOA and ALCOA+ principles.

Chapter 2 includes a very comprehensive primer on good documentation practices/data integrity for paper records, with most of the concepts equally applicable to electronic documentation.

Chapter 3 covers the expectations and examples of risk management considerations for the implementation of ALCOA principles in paper-based and electronic systems.

Chapter 4 discusses the regulatory expectations about good data management practices. It includes U.S. FDA as well as EU, UK, and global guidance documents such as those from WHO, PIC/S, and ISO 13485.

Chapter 5 discusses the consequences of lack of integrity, with comprehensive discussions of the FDA's debarment and disqualifications lists.

Chapter 6 covers data life cycle, one of the most critical concepts associated with good data management and data integrity.

Chapter 7 discusses some examples of how good data management and data integrity must be integrated into the quality management system to ensure that manufacturers provide safe and efficacious medical products.

Chapter 8 presents a summary of how good documentation practices and data integrity are an intrinsic component of good clinical data.

Chapter 9 is probably one of the most important parts of this book. This chapter describes the key elements to prevent data integrity problems, including the implementation of an adequate quality culture.

Chapter 10 describes the primal concept of data governance and how to self-inspect good data management/data integrity principles as part of our quality management control program.

Chapter 11 discusses training program requirements associated with good data management practices and data integrity.

Chapter 12 discusses the critical element of how to investigate data integrity issues and how and when to disclose information about this to regulatory authorities.

Chapter 13 covers the impact of data integrity on the supply chain, including the requirements of clear expectations for data management with suppliers and the strategies to assess it.

Chapter 14 covers the principles associated with maintaining data integrity when using electronic data across the entire life cycle.

The book includes three appendices. Appendix A depicts significant examples of FDA enforcement related to good data management/data integrity. Appendix B describes the content of a three-day data integrity certification course developed by our company. This course is being taught worldwide to regulated companies willing to develop an internal cadre of subject matter experts on this critical topic. Appendix C contains more than 100 ALCOA auditing/assessment questions for both paper and electronic documents and a basic guidance on how to classify those data integrity findings.

I'd like to finish this preface remembering that although most people think data integrity issues are restricted to electronic data systems, mainly within quality control (QC) laboratories, the reality is, based on personal observations, this only represent between 20% and 30% of good data management/data integrity issues within the regulated industry. The main part of data integrity situations relates to poor documentation practices, but regulators are taking very seriously any instance of lack of data integrity, regardless of the causes behind those issues.

Last but not least, I'd like to recognize and say thanks to the Quality Press reviewers for their comments and suggestions, many of which have already been incorporated into the final version of the manuscript. Thanks also to Paul O'Mara and the rest of ASQ's Quality Press staff for your professionalism and devotion to quality.

Thanks to Guillermo Candelario for the preparation of the material included in Appendix C, and thanks to José Andrés Rodríguez-Copeland for his reviews of the manuscript and continuous support.

1

Introduction

1.1 GOOD DATA MANAGEMENT

In recent years, there has been a dramatic escalation in the number of U.S. Food and Drug Administration (FDA) warning letters, World Health Organization (WHO) notices of concern, and European Medicines Agency (EMA) statements of noncompliance in which false or misleading information has been identified during regulatory inspections. Failure to properly manage data integrity applies equally to paper and electronic data. It can arise either from poor systematic control of the data management systems due to a lack of knowledge, careless work, or intentionally hidden, falsified, or misleading data. This is troubling because ensuring data integrity is a critical component of the industry's responsibility to ensure the safety, efficacy, and quality of medical products and of regulators' ability to protect the public health. In the case of the U.S. FDA, these data integrity–related current good manufacturing practice (cGMP) violations have led to numerous regulatory actions, including warning letters, import alerts, and consent decrees.

Data integrity is a global mandatory requirement for the regulated healthcare industry. It is also a basic element of good documentation practices, one of the most fundamental pillars of any quality management system (QMS), including cGMP. Developing and bringing a medical product to market involves different players and activities; therefore, robustness and accuracy of the data submitted by manufacturers to regulatory authorities are crucial. The data must be comprehensive, complete, accurate, and true to ensure the quality of studies supporting applications for medical products to be placed on the market.

Medical product regulatory systems worldwide depend upon the knowledge of companies that develop, manufacture and package, test, distribute, and monitor medical products. Implicit in the assessment and review process is trust between the regulator and the regulated that the information submitted in dossiers and those used in day-to-day decision making is comprehensive, complete, and reliable.

Data integrity is critical throughout the cGMP data life cycle as it enables good decision making by medical product manufacturers and regulatory authorities. It is a fundamental requirement of the medical product quality systems, applying equally to manual (paper) and electronic systems. It is the responsibility of senior management to ensure data integrity through the promotion of a quality culture together with implementation of organizational and technical measures. It requires participation and commitment by staff at all levels within the company, by the company's suppliers, and by its distributors.

Senior management must ensure that data integrity risk is assessed, mitigated, and communicated in accordance with the principles of quality risk management. The effort and resource assigned to data integrity measures must be commensurate with the risk to product quality. Where long-term measures are identified in order to achieve the desired state of control, interim measures must be implemented to mitigate risk, and must be monitored for effectiveness.

Complete, consistent, and accurate data must be attributable, legible, contemporaneous, original, and accurate (ALCOA). These basic ALCOA principles and the related good documentation practice (GDocP) expectations that oversee data reliability are not new, and much high- and mid-level normative guidance already exists. However, in recent years, the number of observations made regarding good data and record management practices during inspections of manufacturing (GMP), clinical (GCP), and laboratory (GLP) has been increasing sharply. The reasons for the increasing concern of regulatory authorities regarding data reliability are multifactorial and include increased regulatory awareness and concern regarding gaps between industry practices and appropriate control strategies.

The way regulatory data is generated has continued to evolve in line with the ongoing development of technologies, such as the increasing use of electronic data capture, automation of systems, and so on. Systems can range from manual processes with paper records to the use of fully computerized systems, but the main purpose of the regulatory requirements remains the same: that is, to have confidence in the quality and the integrity of the data generated (to ensure patient safety and quality of products) and to allow the reconstruction of activities.

Factors contributing to the lack of data integrity include failures by organizations to apply robust systems that inhibit data risks, to improve the detection of situations where data reliability may be compromised, and/or to investigate and address root causes when failures do arise. For example, companies subject to medical product good practice (GXP) requirements have been using validated computerized systems for decades, but many failed to adequately review and manage original electronic records and instead often only review and manage incomplete and/or inappropriate printouts. These observations highlight the need for the industry to modernize control strategies and apply modern quality risk management (QRM) and sound scientific principles to current business models (such as outsourcing and globalization) as well as technologies currently in use (such as computerized systems).

Examples of controls to ensure good data management strategies include, among others:

- A QRM approach that effectively ensures patient safety and product quality and validity of data by ensuring that management aligns expectations with actual process capabilities.

- Monitoring of processes and allocation of the necessary resources by management to ensure and enhance infrastructure, as required (for example, to continuously improve processes and methods, to ensure adequate design and maintenance of buildings, facilities, equipment, and systems; to ensure adequate, reliable power and water supplies; to provide necessary training for personnel; and to allocate the necessary resources to the oversight of contract sites and suppliers to ensure adequate quality standards are met). Active engagement of management in this manner remediates and reduces pressures and possible sources of error that may increase data integrity risks.

- Adoption of a quality culture within the company that encourages personnel to be transparent about failures so that management has an accurate understanding of risks and can then provide the necessary resources to achieve expectations and meet data quality standards: a reporting mechanism independent of management hierarchy must be provided for.

- Mapping of data processes and application of QRM and sound scientific principles throughout the data life cycle.

- Ensuring all personnel are kept up to date about the application of GDocPs to ensure the GXP principles of ALCOA are understood and applied to electronic data in the same manner that has historically been applied to paper records.

- Implementation and confirmation during validation of computerized systems and subsequent change control, so all necessary controls for GDocP for electronic data are in place and the probability of the occurrence of errors in the data is minimized.

- The importance of data integrity to quality assurance and public health protection must be included in personnel training programs. Also, it is necessary to train personnel who use computerized systems and review electronic data in the basic understanding of how computerized systems work and how to efficiently review the electronic data, which includes metadata and audit trails.

- Definition and management of appropriate roles and responsibilities for quality agreements and contracts entered into by clients (contract givers) and suppliers (contract acceptors), including the need for risk-based monitoring of data generated and managed by the supplier organization on behalf of the contract giver.

- Modernization of quality assurance inspection techniques and gathering of quality metrics to efficiently and effectively identify risks and opportunities to improve data processes.

Between 2015 and 2016, major regulatory bodies, such as the EMA, U.S. FDA, WHO, UK Medicines and Healthcare Products Regulatory Agency (MHRA), and Pharmaceutical Inspection Co-operation Scheme (PIC/S), published guidance documents on the topic of data integrity and data management. In the context of these guidelines, good documentation practices are those measures that collectively and individually ensure documentation, whether paper or electronic, is secure, attributable, legible, traceable, permanent, contemporaneously recorded, original, and accurate.

In August 2016, the EMA and the PIC/S[1] announced the publication of a new GMP data integrity guidance document. Data from testing, manufacturing, packaging, distribution, and monitoring of drugs are used by regulators to review the quality, safety, and efficacy of drugs, so ensuring the integrity and completeness of such data is important. This document addresses the assessment of risk to data integrity, risk management strategies, design and control of electronic and paper-based documentation systems, and ensuring data integrity of outside contractors. It appears that regulators are taking a closer look at data integrity industrywide.

The U.S. FDA released its own data integrity draft guidance document in April 2016 (updated as final guidance in December 2018), which relies on numerous prior guidance documents. It reaffirms the critical role of quality functions and quality professionals to ensure integrity of data:

- For recording data, manufacturing or testing steps, numbered and controlled forms must be issued and reconciled by quality assurance (QA)

---

[1]   http://www.picscheme.org/layout/document.php?id=1566. Accessed December 18, 2018.

- Any findings of data integrity violations and "removing at all levels individuals responsible for data integrity problems from GMP positions" must be disclosed to the FDA

- Before batch release, QA must review the audit trail and electronic testing

- Control strategies must be in place to ensure all original lab records (paper and electronic) are reviewed by a person, and all test results are appropriately reported

- Immediate and irreversible recording of electronic testing data, including after completing each high-performance liquid chromatography (HPLC) testing sequence versus recording only at the end of the day

1.2 DATA INTEGRITY AND WHY IT IS SO IMPORTANT

Data integrity is the degree to which data are complete, consistent, accurate, trustworthy, and reliable and that these characteristics of the data are maintained throughout the data life cycle. The data must be collected and maintained in a secure manner, such that they are ALCOA. Ensuring data integrity requires appropriate quality and risk management systems, including adherence to sound scientific principles and GDocPs.

Good data and record management practices are the totality of organized measures that must be in place to collectively and individually ensure that data and records are secure, attributable, legible, traceable, permanent, contemporaneously recorded, original, and accurate and that, if not robustly implemented, can impact data reliability and completeness and undermine the robustness of decision making based upon those data records.

The scope of this book is designated as "GXP" in that everything contained here is GXP unless stated otherwise. The lack of examples specific to a GXP does not mean it is not relevant to that GXP, just that the examples given are not exhaustive.

This book aims to promote a risk-based approach to data management that includes data risk, criticality, and life cycle. Users of this book need to understand their data processes (as a life cycle) to identify data with the greatest GXP impact. From that, the identification of the most effective and efficient risk-based control and review of the data can be determined and implemented.

Every regulated company needs to take responsibility for the systems used and the data they generate. The organizational culture must ensure data are complete, consistent, and accurate in all its forms and media (paper, hybrids, and electronic systems), and senior managers must ensure that they foster the right environment to enable data integrity controls to be effective. For this reason, data governance policies must be endorsed at the highest levels of the regulated company.

Organizations must be aware that reverting from automated or computerized systems to paper-based manual systems or *vice versa* will not in itself remove the need for appropriate data integrity controls. Where data integrity weaknesses are identified, companies must ensure appropriate corrective and preventive actions are globally implemented across all relevant activities and systems.

Good data management practices influence the integrity of all data generated and recorded by a manufacturer, and these practices must ensure data are accurate, complete, and reliable. While the main focus of this book is in relation to data integrity expectations, the principles herein must also be considered in the wider context of good data management. Data integrity applies to all elements of the QMS, and it has become a focal point of regulatory inspections worldwide. To help companies effectively comply with good documentation practices and data integrity principles, the book includes two appendices that can be used for self-inspection and readiness purposes regarding good data management.

1.3 KEY TERMS

The definitions given below apply to the terms used in this book.

ALCOA. This refers to a commonly used acronym for "attributable, legible, contemporaneous, original, and accurate."

A—attributable to the person generating the data

L—legible and permanent

C—contemporaneous

O—original record (or certified true copy)

A—accurate

See Chapter 3 for a detailed description of each principle.

ALCOA+ is used when the following attributes are added to the previous list: complete, consistent, enduring, and available.

Archive. This refers to a designated secure area or facility (for example, cabinet, room, building, or computerized system) for the long-term retention of data and metadata for the purposes of verification of the process or activity.

Audit trail. The audit trail is a form of metadata (see definition below) that contains information associated with actions that relate to the creation, modification, or deletion of GXP records. Audit trail means a secure, computer-generated, time-stamped electronic record that allows for reconstruction of the course of events relating to the creation, modification, or deletion of an electronic record without obscuring or overwriting the original record. An audit trail facilitates the reconstruction of the history of such events relating to the record regardless of its medium, including the "who, what, when, and why" of the action. For example, the audit trail for an HPLC run could include the user name, date/time of the run, the integration parameters used, and details of a reprocessing, if any, including change justification for the reprocessing.

In electronic records, computer-generated audit trails must retain the original entry and document the user identification, the time/date stamp of the action, and the reason for the change, as required to substantiate and justify the action. It may include discrete event logs, history files, database queries or reports or other mechanisms that display events related to the computerized system, specific electronic records, or specific data contained within the record.

In a paper record, an audit trail of a change would be documented via a single-line cross-out that allows the original entry to remain legible and documents the initials of the person making the change, the date of the change, and the reason for the change, as required to substantiate and justify the change.

Backup. This refers to a copy of current (editable) data, metadata and, system configuration settings maintained for recovery, including disaster recovery. A backup means a copy of one or more electronic files created as an alternative in case the original data or system is lost or has become unusable (for example, in the event of a system crash or corruption of a disk). It is important to note that backup differs from archival in that backup copies of electronic records are typically only temporarily stored for the purposes of disaster recovery and may be periodically overwritten. Such temporary backup copies must not be relied upon as an archival mechanism.

The FDA uses the term "backup" in §§ 211.68(b) to refer to a true copy of the original data that is maintained securely throughout the record's retention period (for example, §§ 211.180). The backup file must contain the data (which includes associated metadata) and must be in the original format or in a format compatible with the original format.

This must not be confused with backup copies that may be created during normal computer use and temporarily maintained for disaster recovery (for example, in case of a computer crash or other interruption). Such temporary backup copies would not satisfy the requirement in §§ 211.68(b) to maintain a backup file of data.

Computerized system. A computerized system collectively controls the performance of one or more automated processes and/or functions. It includes computer hardware, software, peripheral devices, networks, and documentation, for example, manuals and standard operating procedures (SOPs), as well as the personnel interfacing with the hardware and software, for example, users and information technology support personnel.

Computerized system transactions. A computerized system transaction is a single operation or sequence of operations performed as a single logical "unit of work." The operation(s) that makes a transaction may not be saved as a permanent record on durable storage until the user commits the transaction through a deliberate act (for example, pressing a save button) or until the system forces the saving of data.

Data. Data means all original records and true copies of original records, including source data and metadata and all subsequent transformations and reports of these data, which are generated or recorded at the time of the GXP activity and allow full and complete reconstruction and evaluation of the GXP activity. Data may be contained in paper records (such as worksheets and logbooks), electronic records and audit trails, photographs, microfilm or microfiche, audio or video files, or any other media whereby information related to GXP activities is recorded.

Data must be "attributable, legible, contemporaneous, original, and accurate" (ALCOA). Data governance measures must also ensure data are complete, consistent, enduring, and available throughout the life cycle (referred to as ALCOA+) where:

- Complete: the data must be whole; a complete set

- Consistent: the data must be in the same format

- Enduring: durable, lasting throughout the data life cycle

- Available: readily available for review or inspection purposes

Data flow map. This refers to a graphical representation of the "flow" of data through an information system.

Data governance. This refers to the totality of arrangements to ensure data, irrespective of the format in which they are generated, are recorded, processed, retained, and used to ensure a complete, consistent, and accurate record throughout the data life cycle.

Data integrity. Data integrity is the degree to which data are complete, consistent, accurate, trustworthy, and reliable and that these characteristics of the data are maintained throughout the data life cycle. The data must be collected and maintained in a secure manner, such that they are attributable, legible, contemporaneously recorded, original or a true copy, and accurate. Assuring data integrity requires appropriate quality and risk management systems, including adherence to sound scientific principles and good documentation practices.

Data life cycle. This refers to all phases of the process by which data are created, recorded, processed, reviewed, analyzed and reported, transferred, stored and retrieved, and monitored until retirement and disposal. There must be a planned approach to assessing, monitoring, and managing the data and the risks to those data in a manner commensurate with potential impact on patient safety, product quality, and/or the reliability of the decisions made throughout all phases of the data life cycle. Data governance must be applied across the entire data life cycle to provide assurance of data integrity. Data can be retained either in the original system, subject to suitable controls, or in an appropriate archive.

The data life cycle refers to how data are generated, processed, reported, checked, used for decision making, stored, and finally discarded at the end of the retention period. Data relating to a product or process may cross various boundaries within the life cycle. This may include data transfer between manual and information technology (IT) systems or between different organizational boundaries: both internal (for example, between production, quality control, and quality assurance) and external (for example, between suppliers and clients). See Chapter 6 for a complete discussion of this topic.

Dynamic record format. Records in dynamic format, such as electronic records, allow for an interactive relationship between the user and the record content. For example, electronic records in database formats allow the user to track, trend, and query data; chromatography records maintained as electronic records allow a user with proper access privileges to reprocess the data and expand the baseline to view the integration more clearly. It also may allow the user to modify formulas or entries in a spreadsheet used to compute test results or other information such as calculated yield.

GXP. This is an acronym for the good practice guides governing the preclinical, clinical, manufacturing, testing, storage, distribution, and postmarked activities for regulated products, such as good laboratory practices, good clinical practices, good manufacturing practices, good distribution practices, good documentation practices, and good pharmacovigilance practices.

Hybrid approach. This refers to the use of a computerized system in which there is a combination of original electronic records and paper records that comprise the total record set that should be reviewed and retained.

Metadata. Metadata are data about data that provide the contextual information required to understand those data. These include structural and descriptive metadata. Such data describe the structure, data elements, interrelationships, and other characteristics of data (for example, audit trails). Metadata also permit data to be attributable to an individual or, if automatically generated, to the original data source.

Metadata necessary to evaluate the meaning of data must be securely linked to the data and subject to adequate review. For example, in weighing, the number 8 is meaningless without metadata (for example, the unit, mg).

Metadata for a particular piece of data could include the time/date stamp of an activity, the operator identification of the person who performed an activity, the instrument used, processing parameters, sequence files, audit trails, and other data required to understand data and reconstruct activities.

Original record. This refers to the first or source capture of data or information: for example, the original paper record of manual observation or electronic raw data file from a computerized system, and all subsequent data required to fully reconstruct the conduct of the GXP activity. Original records can be static or dynamic.

Raw data. Raw data (synonymous with "source data" or "primary data") is defined as the original record (data) that can be described as the first capture of information, whether recorded on paper or electronically. Information that is originally captured in a dynamic state must remain available in that state.

Raw data must permit full reconstruction of the activities. Where this has been captured in a dynamic state and generated electronically, paper copies cannot be considered as raw data.

In the case of basic electronic equipment that does not store electronic data or provides only a printed data output (for example, balances or pH meters), then the printout constitutes the raw data. Where the basic electronic equipment does store electronic data permanently and only holds a certain volume before overwriting, these data must be periodically reviewed and where necessary reconciled against paper records and extracted as electronic data where this is supported by the equipment itself. In all definitions, the term "data" includes raw data.

Static record format. A static record format, such as a paper or Portable Document Format (PDF) record, is one that is fixed and allows little or no interaction between the user and the record content. For example, once printed or converted to static PDFs, chromatography records lose the capability of being reprocessed or enabling more detailed viewing of baselines.

True copy. A true copy is a copy (irrespective of the type of media used) of an original recording of data that has been verified and certified to confirm it is an exact and complete copy that preserves the entire content and meaning of the original record, including, in the case of electronic data, all essential metadata and the original record format as appropriate. Verification of a true copy can be accomplished by a dated signature or by generation through an automated and validated process.

1.4 GOOD DOCUMENTATION PRACTICES: ALCOA AND ALCOA+

The basic building blocks of good GXP data are to follow good documentation practices and then to manage risks to the accuracy, completeness, consistency, and reliability of the data throughout their entire period of usefulness, that is, throughout the data life cycle.

Personnel must follow good documentation practices for both paper records and electronic records to ensure the integrity of the data. These principles require that documentation has the characteristics of being ALCOA. These essential characteristics apply equally to both paper and electronic records.

- **Attributable.** This means information is captured in the record so it is uniquely identified as executed by the originator of the data (for example, a person or a computer system).

- **Legible, traceable, and permanent.** The terms legible, traceable, and permanent refer to the requirements that data are readable and understandable and allow a clear picture of the sequencing of steps or events in the record so all GXP activities conducted can be fully reconstructed by the people reviewing these records at any point during the record's retention period.

- **Contemporaneous.** Contemporaneous data are data recorded at the time they are generated or observed.

- **Original.** Original data include the first or source capture of data or information and all subsequent data required to fully reconstruct the conduct of the GXP activity. The GXP requirements for original data include the following:

  - Original data must be reviewed

  - Original data and/or true and verified copies that preserve the content and meaning of the original data must be retained

  - Original records must be complete, enduring, and readily retrievable and readable throughout the record's retention period

- **Accurate.** The term "accurate" means data are correct, truthful, complete, valid, and reliable.

Implicit in the above-listed requirements for ALCOA is that the records must be complete, consistent, enduring, and available. To emphasize these requirements, this is sometimes referred to as ALCOA+.

- **Complete.** All information is provided to recreate an event. A complete record of data generated electronically includes relevant metadata.

- **Consistent.** Good documentation practices apply throughout any process—no exception.

- **Enduring.** Records must exist for the entire period during which they might be needed. They need to remain intact and accessible as an indelible/enduring record throughout the record retention period.

- **Available.** Records must be available for authorized review at any time during the required retention period.

Published regulatory guidance documents embrace the acronym ALCOA rather than "ALCOA+." ALCOA was historically regarded as defining the attributes of data quality that are suitable for regulatory purposes. The "+" has been subsequently added to emphasize the requirements. There is no difference in expectations regardless of which acronym is used since data governance measures must ensure data are complete, consistent, enduring, and available throughout the data life cycle.

Further guidance to aid understanding as to how these requirements apply in each case and the special risk considerations that may need to be taken into account during implementation is provided in Chapter 3.

1.5 APPLICABILITY

Good documentation practices and data integrity are critical elements of the medical product quality systems and are also requirements for clinical trial documentation. A systematic approach must be implemented to provide a high level of assurance that throughout the product life cycle, all GXP records and data are complete and reliable. Among the products covered by good documentation practices and data integrity principles are:

- Pharmaceutical

- Medical devices

- Combination products

- Human subject laboratories

- Clinical trials data

- Cosmetics

- Food

- Dietary supplements

- Veterinary

Applicability to both paper and electronic data. The requirements for good documentation practices and data integrity that ensure robust control of data validity apply equally to paper and electronic data, and all hybrid systems. Organizations subject to GXP must be fully aware that reverting from automated or computerized to manual or paper-based systems does not in itself remove the need for robust management controls.

Applicability to clients (contract givers) and suppliers (contract acceptors). The principles of data integrity apply to clients and suppliers. Clients (contract givers) are ultimately responsible for the robustness of all decisions made on the basis of GXP data, including those made on the basis of data provided to them by suppliers (contract acceptors). Clients must therefore perform risk-based due diligence to assure themselves that suppliers have in place appropriate programs to ensure the veracity, completeness, and reliability of the data provided.

1.6 QUALITY RISK MANAGEMENT AND DATA INTEGRITY

Regulated companies are expected to implement, design, and operate a documented system that provides an acceptable state of control based on the data integrity risk and that it is fully documented with supporting rationale.

An example of a suitable approach is to perform a data integrity risk assessment where the processes that produce data or where data are obtained are mapped out, each of the formats and their controls is identified, and the data criticality and inherent risks are documented. The effort and resource applied to ensure the integrity of the data must be commensurate with the risk and impact of a data integrity failure to the patient or consumer. Together these arrangements fulfill the concept of data governance.

Risk management principles are described in documents such as the International Conference on Harmonization (ICH) Q9 Quality Risk Management (applying to pharmaceuticals), the International Standard ISO 14971 (applying to medical devices), and the ICH E6, which applies to clinical trials.[2]

Robust decision making requires appropriate quality and risk management systems and adherence to sound scientific and statistical principles, which must be based upon reliable data. For example, the scientific principle of being an objective, unbiased observer regarding the outcome of a sample analysis requires that suspect results be investigated and excluded from the reported results only if they are clearly attributable to an identified cause. Adhering to good data and record-keeping principles requires that any rejected results be recorded, together with a documented justification for their rejection, and that this documentation is subject to review and retention. Section 7.7.1 expands on this topic.

Regulated companies must establish, implement, and maintain an appropriate quality management system. The quality manual, or another high-level document, must include, as part of the commitment to an effective quality management system, a code of ethics and code of proper conduct to ensure the reliability and completeness of data, including mechanisms for staff to report any quality and compliance questions or concerns to management.

---

[2]   The book *Quality Risk Management for the FDA-Regulated Industry* (Rodríguez-Pérez, 2017) can be used as source of information on the topics of risk management for the regulated industry.

Within the quality management system, the company must establish the appropriate infrastructure, organizational structure, written policies and procedures, processes, and systems to both prevent and detect situations that may impact data integrity and, in turn, the risk-based and scientific robustness of decisions based upon those data.

The risk-based approach to record and data management must ensure adequate resources are allocated and control strategies for the assurance of the integrity of data are commensurate with their potential impact on product quality, patient safety, and related decision making. Strategies that promote good practices and prevent record and data integrity issues from occurring are preferred and are likely to be the most effective and cost-effective actions.

Data integrity risks must be assessed, mitigated, communicated, and reviewed throughout the data life cycle in accordance with the principles of risk management. Data have varying importance to quality, safety, and efficacy decisions. Data criticality may be determined by considering how the data are used to influence the decisions made.

When long-term measures are identified in order to achieve the desired state of control, interim measures must be implemented to mitigate risk and must be monitored for effectiveness. Where interim measures or risk prioritization are required, residual data integrity risk must be communicated to senior management and kept under review. Reverting from automated/computerized to paper-based systems will not remove the need for data governance. Moreover, such retrograde approaches are likely to increase administrative burden and data risk.

Not all data or processing steps have the same importance to product quality and patient safety. Risk management must be utilized to determine the importance of each data/processing step. An effective risk management approach to data governance will consider:

- Data criticality: impact to decision making and product quality

- Data risk: opportunity for data alteration and deletion, and likelihood of detection or visibility of changes by the manufacturer's routine review processes

Assessing data criticality. The decision that data influences may differ in importance and the impact of the data to a decision may also vary. Points to consider regarding data criticality include:

- Which decision does the data influence? For example, when making a batch release decision, data that determine compliance with critical quality attributes are of greater importance than warehouse cleaning records.

- What is the impact of the data to product quality or safety? For example, for an oral tablet, active substance assay data are of generally greater impact to product quality and safety than tablet friability data.

Assessing data risk. Data risk assessment must consider the vulnerability of data to involuntary or deliberate alteration, falsification, deletion, loss or re-creation, and the likelihood of detection of such actions. Consideration must also be given to ensuring complete data recovery in the event of a disaster. Control measures that prevent unauthorized activity and increase visibility and/or detectability can be used as risk-mitigating actions.

Risk assessments must focus on business processes (for example production, quality control, and so on), evaluate data flows and the methods of generating data, and not just consider IT system functionality or complexity. Factors to consider include:

- Process complexity

- Methods of generating, storing, and retiring data and their ability to ensure data accuracy, legibility, and indelibility

- Process consistency and degree of automation and human interaction

- Subjectivity of outcome/result (for example, is the process open ended or well defined?)

- The outcome of a comparison between electronic system data and manually recorded events could be indicative of malpractice (for example, apparent discrepancies between analytical reports and raw data acquisition times)

For computerized systems, manual interfaces with IT systems must be considered in the risk assessment process. Computerized system validation in isolation may not result in low data integrity risk, in particular when the user is able to influence the reporting of data from the validated system.

A company that believes there is "no risk" of data integrity failure is unlikely to have made an adequate assessment of inherent risks in the data life cycle. On the other hand, regulated companies are not expected to implement a forensic approach to data checking on a routine basis. Systems must maintain appropriate levels of control while wider data governance measures must ensure periodic self-inspections or audits can detect opportunities for data integrity failures within the company's systems.

1.7 DATA QUALITY AND DATA INTEGRITY

This book primarily addresses data integrity and not data quality since the controls required for integrity do not necessarily guarantee the quality of the data generated. People struggle to differentiate between integrity and quality. In the last few years, the regulated industry has become familiar with the definition and attributes of data integrity, and ALCOA is now a well-known concept. We even can distinguish between ALCOA and ALCOA+ as previously established in Section 1.4.

"Data quality" is a more comprehensive term that includes integrity. We can define data quality as the *usefulness of data*. Many people might consider quality and integrity as similar, but in fact they are not: it is possible to have integrity without quality, but not quality without integrity.

In the production of medical or regulated products, we can find situations where we have data integrity without data quality. For example, during the validation of a manufacturing process, sampling plans for process control were not properly developed and established. As a consequence, the samples that are taken to monitor the performance of the process are not representative of the process. These samples are taken and analyzed, and the results are reported following all principles of data integrity (ALCOA). We can consider data obtained from this process as attributable, legible, contemporaneous, original, and accurate. However, from the point of view of the usefulness of the data, it has no quality because the data do not statistically represent the process.

2

Data Integrity and Good Documentation Practices

2.1 TYPE OF DATA

Data may be generated by:

a. Recording on paper, using a paper-based record of a manual observation or of an activity

b. Electronically, using equipment that ranges from simple machines to complex, highly configurable computerized systems

c. By using a hybrid system where both paper-based and electronic records constitute the original record

d. By other means such as photography, imagery, chromatography plates, and so on

Paper. Data generated manually on paper may require independent verification if deemed necessary from the data integrity risk assessment or by another requirement (for example, regulatory requirements to verification of critical or significant manufacturing steps). Consideration must be given to risk-reducing supervisory measures.

Electronic. The intrinsic risks to data integrity relating to equipment and computerized systems may vary depending upon the degree to which the system generating or using the data can be configured and the potential for manipulation of data during transfer between computerized systems during the data life cycle. The use of available technology, suitably configured to reduce data integrity risk, must be a prime consideration.

Simple electronic systems with no configurable software and no electronic data retention (for example pH meters, balances, thermometers, and similar ones) may only require calibration, whereas complex systems will require "validation for intended purpose."

Validation effort increases with complexity and risk (determined by software functionality, configuration, the opportunity for user intervention, and data life cycle considerations). It is important not to overlook systems of apparent lower complexity. Within these systems, it may be possible to manipulate data or repeat testing to achieve the desired outcome with limited opportunity for detection. Special care must be taken with standalone systems with a user-configurable output such as electrocardiogram (ECG) machines, Fourier-transform infrared spectrometers, and ultraviolet spectrophotometers, among others.

Hybrid. Where hybrid systems are used, what constitutes the data set must be clearly documented, and all records that are defined by the data set must be reviewed and retained. Hybrid systems must be designed to ensure they meet the desired objective.

Other. Where the data generated are captured by a photograph or imagery (or other media), the requirements for storage of that format throughout its life cycle must follow the same considerations of the other formats, including any additional controls required for that format.

Where the original format cannot be retained due to degradation issues, alternative mechanisms for recording (for example, photography or digitization) and subsequent storage may be considered and the selection rationale documented (for example, thin-layer chromatography).

Reduced effort and/or frequency of control measures may be justified for data that have a lesser impact on product quality or patient safety if those data are obtained from a process that does not provide the opportunity for amendment without high-level system access or specialist software knowledge.

The data integrity risk assessment must consider factors required to follow a process or perform a function. It is expected to consider not only a computerized system, but also the supporting people, guidance, training, and quality systems. Therefore, automation or the use of a validated system, such as analytical equipment may lower but not eliminate data integrity risk. Where there is human intervention, particularly influencing how or what data are recorded, reported, or retained, an increased risk may exist from poor organizational controls or data verification due to an overreliance on the system's validated state.

Where the data integrity risk assessment has highlighted areas for remediation, prioritization of actions (including acceptance of an appropriate level of residual risk) must be documented, communicated to management, and subject to review. In situations where long-term remediation actions are identified, risk-reducing, short-term measures must be implemented to provide acceptable data governance in the interim.

2.2 DESIGN OF RECORD-KEEPING METHODOLOGIES AND SYSTEMS: CREATING THE "RIGHT ENVIRONMENT"

Record-keeping systems and processes, whether paper or electronic, must be designed in a way that facilitates and encourages compliance with the principles of data integrity for all kinds of records. Enablers of a compliant and desired behavior include:

- At the point of use, having access to appropriately controlled/synchronized clocks for recording timed events to ensure reconstruction and traceability, knowing and specifying the time zone where this data is used across multiple sites. Restricting the ability to change any clock used for recording timed events (for example, system clocks in electronic systems and process instrumentation).

- Accessibility of controlled forms for recording GXP data (for example, paper batch records, paper case report forms (CRFs), laboratory worksheets, and so on) at locations where activities take place so informal data recording and later transcription to official records are not necessary.

- Controlling the issuance of blank paper templates for data recording of GXP activities so all printed forms can be reconciled and accounted for. Reconciliation, or the use of controlled books with numbered pages, may be necessary to prevent re-creation of a record. There may be exceptions such as medical records controlled by good clinical practices where this is not practical.

- Restricting user access rights to automated systems to prevent (or audit trail, if prevention is not possible) unauthorized data amendments. Use of external devices or system interfacing methods that eliminate manual data entries and human interaction with the computerized system, such as barcode scanners, ID card readers, or printers.

- The provision of a work environment (such as adequate space and resources, enough time for tasks, and properly functioning equipment) that permits performance of tasks and recording of data as required.

- Ensuring automated data capture or printers are attached and connected to equipment, such as balances, to ensure independent and timely recording of the data. Ensuring proximity of printers to sites of relevant activities.

- Ensuring ease of access to locations of sampling points (for example, sampling points for water systems) to allow easy and efficient performance of sampling by the operators and therefore minimizing the temptation to take shortcuts or falsify samples.

- Ensuring access to original records for staff performing data review activities.

- Providing sufficient training in data integrity principles to all appropriate staff, including senior management.

- Senior management oversight of quality metrics relevant to data governance.

- Inclusion of subject matter experts in the risk assessment process.

Data and record media must be durable. For paper records, the ink must be indelible. Temperature-sensitive or photosensitive inks and other erasable inks must not be used. Paper must also not be temperature sensitive or photosensitive. If this is not feasible or limited (as may be the case in printouts from legacy printers of balances and other instruments in production and quality control laboratories), then true or certified copies must be prepared until this equipment is retired or replaced.

Maintenance of record-keeping systems. The systems implemented and maintained for both paper and electronic record keeping must take account of scientific and technical progress. Systems, procedures, and methodologies used to record and store data must be periodically reviewed for effectiveness and updated as necessary.

2.3 PROCEDURE FOR GOOD DOCUMENTATION PRACTICES/DATA INTEGRITY IN PAPER

The following expectations must be implemented using a quality risk management approach, considering the risk and criticality of data recorded.

Is it required by the regulatory authorities to implement a specific procedure for data integrity? As of the time of this writing, there is no specific requirement for such procedure in any of the major regulations (U.S. FDA, UE's EMA, UK's MHRAs, PIC/S, or WHO). Today, most regulated companies have a good documentation practice procedure including basic instructions regarding the color of ink that can be used to fill out records, how to make corrections, and so on. On the other hand, very few companies have a formal procedure laying out the principles of data integrity and its governance. It is highly recommended, although not yet mandatory, that each regulated company formalizes those data integrity principles.

The rest of this chapter covers (from 2.3.1 to 2.3.11) the basic elements of good documentation practices and data integrity governance for paper records, while Chapter 14 covers specific elements of data integrity for electronic data.

Following are the minimum requirements for GDocPs that must be considered at the different phases of the life cycle of regulated documents and records.

2.3.1 Generation of documents and records

a. All documents must have a unique identification number (including the version number) and must be checked, approved, signed, and dated

b. The use of uncontrolled (unapproved) documents must be prohibited by procedures

c. The use of temporary recording practices, such as scrap papers or Post-it Notes, must also be prohibited

d. The document design must provide sufficient space for manual data entries

e. The document design must make it clear what data are to be provided in entries

f. The document design must be structured in such a way as to record information in the same order as the operational process

g. Documents must be stored in a manner that ensures appropriate version control

h. Master copies of documents must be prevented from unauthorized or inadvertent changes

i. For template records stored electronically, the following precautions must be in place:

   i. Access to master templates must be controlled

   ii. Process controls for creating and updating versions must be clear and practically applied and verified

    iii. Master documents must be stored in a manner that prevents unauthorized changes

Potential areas of concern and risk management considerations

- Uncontrolled (unapproved) documents increase the potential for omission or loss of critical data, as these documents may not be designed to correctly record critical data

- It may be easier to falsify uncontrolled records

- There is a risk of using obsolete documents when no version control or control for issuance is established

- Handwriting data may not be clear and legible if the spaces provided for data entry are not sufficiently sized

- Data should not be completed on the reverse (unused side) of existing pages, as this would typically be omitted when copied

- If additional pages of the documents are added to allow complete documentation, the number of additional pages and reference to any pages added must be clearly documented on the main record page and signed

- Ambiguous instructions may lead to inconsistent or incorrect recording of data

- Inappropriate storage conditions of documents and records can allow unauthorized modification, use of obsolete and/or draft documents, or cause the loss of master documents

- The processes of implementation and effective communication are as important as the document

- Completion of entries could not be clear, contemporaneous, and indelible/durable

- Master copies must contain distinctive marking so to distinguish the master from a copy (for example, using colored papers or inks so as to prevent inadvertent use)

2.3.2 Distribution and control of documents and records

    a. Updated versions must be distributed in a timely manner

    b. Obsolete master documents and files must be archived and their access restricted

   c. Any issued and unused physical document must be retrieved and destroyed accordingly

   d. Issue must be controlled by written procedures that include, at least, the following controls:

      i. Using a secure stamp or paper color code/type not available in the working areas or another appropriate system

      ii. Ensuring only the current approved version is available for use

      iii. Allocating a unique identifier to each blank document issued and recording the issue of each document in a register (logbook or similar)

         ○ Numbering every distributed copy (for example, copy 2 of 2) and sequential numbering of issued pages in bound books

         ○ Where the reissue of additional copies of the blank template is necessary, a controlled process regarding reissue must be followed; all distributed copies must be maintained and a justification and approval for the need of an extra copy must be recorded (for example, "the original template record was damaged")

         ○ All issued records must be reconciled following use to ensure the accuracy and completeness of records

   e. An index of all the template records must be maintained by the quality assurance organization. This index must, at the very least, include for each type of template record the following information: title, reference number, including version number, location, effective date, and next review date.

Potential areas of concern and risk management considerations

- Ensure no obsolete or unapproved versions of documents and records are used. There may be a risk that obsolete or unapproved versions can be used by mistake or intentionally if available for use.

- Without the use of security measures, there is a risk that rewriting, or falsification of data, may be made after photocopying or scanning the template record (which gives the user another template copy to use).

- A filled record with an anomalous data entry could be replaced by a new rewritten template.

- All unused forms must be accounted for, and either defaced and destroyed, or returned for secure filing.

2.3.3 Use and control of records within production areas

a. Records must be appropriately controlled in the production areas by designated persons or processes in accordance with written procedures

b. These controls must be carried out to minimize the risk of damage or loss of the records and ensure data integrity

c. Where necessary, measures must be taken to protect records from being soiled (for example, getting wet or stained by materials)

Potential areas of concern and risk management considerations

Same areas of concern in the previous section apply.

2.3.4 Filling out records

a. Handwritten entries must be made by the person who executed the task.

b. Unused, blank fields within documents must be crossed out and signed.

c. Do not allow the use of unknown symbols and/or abbreviation, such as the use of ditto (") marks.

d. Handwritten entries must be made in clear and legible writing.

e. The use of personal seals is generally not encouraged; however, where used, seals must be controlled for access. There must be a log that clearly shows traceability between an individual and their personal seal. Use of personal seals must be dated by the owner to be deemed acceptable.

f. The completion of date fields must be done in the format defined by the company.

g. Records must be enduring (indelible).

h. Records must be signed and dated using a unique identifier that is attributable to the author.

i. Filling out operations must be contemporaneous. The use of a scribe to record an activity on behalf of another operator must be considered only on an exceptional basis. Section 3.1 includes a discussion of this topic.

Potential areas of concern and risk management considerations

- Check that handwriting is consistent for entries made by the same person.

- Check that entries are legible and clear (do not include the use of unknown symbols/abbreviations, such as the use of ditto ["] marks).

- Check for completeness of data recorded.

- Check correct pagination of the records and that all pages are present.

- Verify that records are available within the immediate areas in which they are used. If the form is not available at the point of use, this will not allow operators to fill in records at the time of occurrence.

- Check that written entries are in ink, which is not erasable and/or will not smudge or fade during the retention period.

- Check that the records were not filled out using pencil prior to use of pen (overwriting).

- Note that some paper printouts from systems may fade over time (for example, thermal paper).

- Check that there are signature and initials logs and that they are controlled and current and demonstrate the use of unique entries, not just standardized printed letters.

- Ensure that all key entries are signed and dated, particularly if steps occur over time (in other words, not just signed at the end of the page and/or process).

2.3.5 Making corrections on records

Here we will distinguish between immediate (contemporaneous) corrections and after-date ones.

Contemporaneous corrections by the same person that made the original entry

a. Cross out what is to be changed with a single line without obscuring the original data

b. Where appropriate, the reason for the correction must be clearly recorded and verified by a second person (supervisor or quality personnel)

c. Initial and date the change made

d. Corrections must be made in indelible ink

e. For significant/critical corrections, the signature of a supervisor/manager must be required, and if necessary, quality assurance might also review the contemporaneous correction

After-date corrections

a. A procedure must describe the handling and verification of after-date corrections to quality system records.

b. If the correction is to fill out missing information (for example, missing signature or missing date or time), the procedure must establish how to perform these corrections and the level of oversight/approval required for each case. In the case of significant/critical corrections (for example, missing or change of a test value), a formal deviation or nonconformance must be required.

c. If possible, the same person who did the original data entry must be the one making the after-date correction. If the person is no longer working with the company or is out of work that day, a supervisor or group leader must be performing the after-date correction.

d. It is highly recommendable to have quality assurance reviewing and signing all after-date corrections.

e. Cross out what is to be changed with a single line without obscuring the original data.

f. The reason for the correction must be clearly recorded and verified.

g. Initial and date the change made.

h. Corrections must be made in indelible ink.

Potential areas of concern and risk management considerations

- Check that the original data are readable and not obscured (for example, not obscured by use of liquid paper; overwriting is not permitted)

- If changes have been made to critical data entries, verify that a valid reason for the change has been recorded and that supporting evidence for the change is available

- Check for unexplained symbols or entries in records

- Check that written entries are in ink, which is not erasable and/or will not smudge or fade (during the retention period)

- Check that the records were not filled out using pencil prior to use of pen (overwriting)

- Frequent corrections are a signal of careless work, lack of adequate training, and lack of effective supervision

2.3.6 Verification of records

a. Production records of *critical process steps* must be reviewed according to an approved procedure as follows:

    i. Reviewed/witnessed by designated personnel (for example, a second worker or a production supervisor) at the time of operations occurring.

    ii. Reviewed by an authorized person within production before sending them to the quality department.

    iii. Reviewed and approved by the quality assurance group (such as authorized person/qualified person or batch release area) before release or distribution of the batch produced.

b. Production records of *noncritical process steps* should be reviewed by production personnel according to an approved procedure before sending them to the quality department.

c. Laboratory testing records must be reviewed by designated personnel (for example a second analyst) following completion of the testing. Reviewers must check all entries and calculations.

d. These verification actions must be conducted after performing production-related tasks and activities. This verification must be signed or initialed and dated by the appropriate persons.

e. A double check is needed to ensure all activities have been completed correctly using the current (approved) documents and records and that the data was critically compared to the acceptance criteria.

f. The secondary review of data must include a verification of any calculation used or performed.

Note: Critical process steps, such as weighing or adding components, must require that the verifier witnesses the activity if performed manually, while other verification activities (for example, the verification of cleaning records or calculation of yield) can be completed later by evaluating the records.

On September 8, 2008 (73 FR 51933), the FDA published a final rule amending certain cGMP requirements for finished pharmaceuticals. This rule included the revision of cGMP requirements concerning verification of performance of operations by a second individual. cGMP regulations include several provisions requiring that certain significant activities be performed by one person and verified as specified by a second person. The FDA proposed to revise Sec. § 211.101(c) or (d), § 211.103, § 211.182, or § 211.188(b) (11) when the operations are performed by automated equipment, such as the widespread and increasing use of computer-controlled operations. These regulations were amended to indicate that, when automated equipment is used to perform certain operations, only one person is needed to verify that the automated equipment is functioning adequately.

The FDA pointed out that "although increasingly sophisticated controls and safeguards have been implemented for some automated systems, policy has been that some degree of human oversight, supervision, verification, monitoring, or checking is still necessary to verify proper performance as part of assuring the identity, strength, quality, and purity of drug products. For suitably validated automated systems, even with real-time time alarms, it is still necessary for a human to verify that the systems are operating as planned and to monitor for abnormalities. The FDA agreed that the level, nature, and frequency of such human verification will vary depending on the level of automation used as well as the nature of the system and controls, and the manufacturer has the flexibility and responsibility to determine what is suitable and necessary." The rule was effective December 8, 2008.

As an example, Sec. § 211.101 "Charge-in of components" was amended by revising paragraphs (c) and (d) to read as follows:

(c) Weighing, measuring, or subdividing operations for components shall be adequately supervised. Each container of component dispensed to manufacturing shall be examined by a second person to assure that:

(1) *The component was released by the quality control unit.*

(2) *The weight or measure is correct as stated in the batch production records.*

(3) *The containers are properly identified. If the weighing, measuring, or subdividing operations are performed by automated equipment under Sec. § 211.68, only one person is needed to assure paragraphs (c)(1), (c)(2), and (c)(3) of this section.*

(d) *Each component shall either be added to the batch by one person and verified by a second person or, if the components are added by automated equipment under Sec. § 211.68, only verified by one person.*

Potential areas of concern and risk management considerations

- Verify the process for the handling of production records within processing areas to ensure they are readily available to the correct personnel at the time of performing the activity to which the record relates

- Verify that any secondary checks performed during processing were performed by appropriately qualified and independent personnel as defined by procedure

- Check that documents were reviewed by production and then quality personnel following completion of operational activities

2.3.7 Maintaining records

a. Companies must implement defined systems for storage and retrieval of records

b. All records must be stored in the specified location in a traceable and accessible manner

c. Systems must ensure all GMP/GDocP-relevant records are stored for periods that meet GMP/GDocP internal and regulatory requirements

d. All records must be protected from damage or destruction by:

    i. Fire

    ii. Liquids (for example water, solvents and buffer solutions in the case of the quality control laboratory)

iii. Pests, such as rodents and insects

iv. High humidity

v. Unauthorized personnel, who may attempt to amend, destroy, or replace records

e. Company must have a procedure describing the strategy for recovering documents after a disaster situation

Potential areas of concern and risk management considerations

- Check if the records are stored in an orderly manner and are easily identifiable.

- Check if there are systems in place to protect records from situations like pest control and sprinklers:
  Note: Sprinkler systems can be implemented if they are designed to prevent damage to documents. For example, documents are protected from water by covering them with plastic film.

- Check if system is in place for the recovery of records in a disaster situation.

2.3.8 Direct printouts from electronic systems

a. Paper records generated by simple electronic systems, such as balances, pH meters, or simple processing equipment, that do not store data provide limited opportunity to influence the presentation of data by (re)processing or changing of electronic date/ timestamps

b. In these situations, the original record must be signed and dated by the person generating the record and the original must be attached to batch processing records

c. If original printout record is not permanent (for example, a thermal printer record), a true copy on a permanent media must be prepared

Potential areas of concern and risk management considerations

- Ensure printouts are signed and dated

- Verify that printout records are made in durable, nonfading media

2.3.9 True copies

Copies of original paper records (for example, analytical summary reports, validation reports, and so on) are generally very useful for communication purposes, such as between companies operating at different locations or with regulatory authorities. These records must be controlled during their life cycle to ensure the data received from another site (sister company, contractor, or supplier) are maintained as "true copies" where appropriate or used as a "summary report" where the requirements of a "true copy" are not met (for example, summary of complex analytical data).

It is conceivable for raw data generated by electronic means to be retained in an acceptable paper or PDF format, where it can be justified that a *static record* maintains the integrity of the original data. However, the data retention process must be shown to include verified copies of all raw data, metadata, relevant audit trail and result files, software/system configuration settings specific to each analytical run, and all data processing runs (including methods and audit trails) necessary for reconstruction of a given raw data set. It would also require a documented means to verify that the printed records were an accurate representation of the original.

However, many electronic records must be maintained in their *dynamic* (electronic) format to enable interaction with the data. Data must be retained in a dynamic form where this is critical to its integrity or later verification. This must be justified based on risk. Documents must be appropriately authenticated as "true copies" either using handwritten or digital signatures.

How must the "true copy" be issued and controlled?

a. At the facility *that issues* the true copy:

   i. Creating a "true copy" of a *paper* document:

      o Obtain the original of the document to be copied.

      o Photocopy the original document, ensuring no information from the original copy is lost.

      o Verify the authenticity of the copied document and sign and date the new hardcopy as a "true copy."

      o The "true copy" may now be sent to the intended recipient.

   ii. Creating a "true copy" of an *electronic* document:

      o A "true copy" of an electronic record must be created by electronic means (electronic file copy), including all required metadata. Creating PDF versions of electronic data must be discouraged, as this is equivalent to a printout from the electronic system, which risks loss of metadata.

   o The "true copy" may now be sent to the intended recipient.

   iii. A distribution list of all issued "true copies" (soft/hard) must be maintained.

b. At the facility that *receives* the true copy:

   i. The paper version, scanned copy, or electronic file must be reviewed and filed according to good document management processes.

   ii. The document must clearly indicate that it is a true copy and not an original record.

   iii. A quality agreement must be in place to address the responsibilities for the generation and transfer of "true copies" and data integrity controls. The system for the issuance and control of "true copies" must be audited by the client (contract giver) and supplier (contract receiver) to ensure the process is robust and meets data integrity principles.

Potential areas of concern and risk management considerations

- Verify the procedure for the generation of true copies.

- Check that true copies issued are identical (complete and accurate) to original records.

- Copied records must be checked against the original document records to make sure there is no tampering of the scanned image.

- Check that scanned or saved records are protected to ensure data integrity.

- After scanning paper records and verifying the creation of a "true copy," it may be possible to permit destruction of the original documents from which the scanned images have been created. Verify that there is a documented approval process for this destruction.

- Ensure received records are checked and retained appropriately.

- A system must be in place to verify the authenticity of "true copies," such as through verification of the correct signatories.

2.3.10 Document retention

a. The retention period of each type of record must (at a minimum) meet those periods specified by GMP/GDP procedures and regulatory requirements

b. The records can be retained internally or by using an outside storage service subject to quality agreements

c. A system must be in place that describes the different steps for archiving records such as identification of archive boxes, list of records by box, retention period, archiving location, and so on

d. All hardcopy quality records must be archived:

   i. In secure locations to prevent damage or loss

   ii. In such a manner that it is easily retrievable

   iii. To ensure records are likely durable for their archived life

e. The company must develop a written, formal strategy for disaster recovery

Potential area of concern and risk management considerations

- Verify if procedures establish the retention period of each type of document/record

- Verify if a risk assessment is available to demonstrate that retention systems/facilities/services are suitable and that the residual risks are understood

- Check that the system implemented for retrieving archived records is effective and traceable

- Check that access to archived documents is restricted to authorized personnel ensuring integrity of the stored records

- Check if the storage methods used must permit efficient retrieval of documents when required

- Check for the outsourced archived operations and whether there is a quality agreement in place and the outsourced storage location was audited

- Ensure there is some assessment of whether documents will still be legible/available for the entire archival period

- Check that access to archived documents is restricted to authorized personnel ensuring integrity of the stored records

- The storage methods used must permit efficient retrieval of documents when required

2.3.11 Disposal of original records

a. A documented process for the disposal of records must be in place to ensure the correct original records are disposed of after the defined retention period

b. The system must ensure current records are not destroyed by accident and that historical records do not inadvertently make their way back into the current record stream (for example, historical records confused/mixed with existing records)

c. A record/register must be available to demonstrate appropriate and timely destruction of retired records

d. Measures must be in place to reduce/minimize the risk of deleting the wrong documents

e. The access rights allowing deletion of records must be limited to few persons

f. In case of printouts that are not permanent (for example, thermo transfer paper), a verified ("true") copy may be retained, and it is possible to discard the nonpermanent original

g. Paper records may be replaced by scans, provided that the principles of "true copy" are addressed

Potential area of concern and risk management considerations

- Verify if there is a procedure covering the disposal of original records

- Verify the register where destruction of original records is documented

- Check how the access rights allowing destruction of records are limited

- Verify if paper records stored as scans (such as PDF copies) meet the "true copy" principles

3

ALCOA: Expectations and Examples

Organizations must follow good documentation practices to ensure the accuracy, completeness, consistency, and reliability of the records and data throughout their entire period of usefulness, that is, throughout the data life cycle. The principles require that documentation must have the characteristics of being ALCOA.

The tables in this chapter provide further guidance on the implementation of the general ALCOA requirements for both paper and electronic records and systems. In addition, examples of special risk management considerations are provided along with several illustrative examples of how these measures are typically implemented.

These examples aid in understanding the concepts and show how successful risk-based implementation might be achieved.

3.1 ATTRIBUTABLE

Attributable means information is captured in the record so that it is uniquely identified as having been executed by the originator of the data (for example, a person or computer system). Table 3.1 depicts the characteristics of attributable records for both paper and electronic ones.

Potential areas of concern and risk management considerations to ensure that actions and records are attributed to a unique individual

- For legally binding signatures, there must be a verifiable, secure link between the unique, identifiable (actual) person signing and the signature event. Signatures must be permanently linked to the

Table 3.1 Attributable records

Attributable	
Expectations for paper records	**Expectations for electronic records**
Attribution of actions in paper records must occur, as appropriate, through the use of: • Initials • Full handwritten signature • Personal seal • Date and, when necessary, time	Attribution of actions in electronic records must occur, as appropriate, through the use of: • Unique user logins that link the user to actions that create, modify, or delete data • Unique electronic signatures (can be either biometric or nonbiometric) • An audit trail that must capture user identification (ID) and date- and timestamps • Signatures, which must be securely and permanently linked to the record being signed

record being signed. Systems that use one application for signing a document and another to store the document being signed must ensure the two remain linked to ensure the attribution is not broken.

• Signatures and personal seals must be executed at the time of performance or review of the event or action being recorded.

• Use of a personal seal to sign documents requires additional risk management controls, such as handwritten dates and procedures that require storage of the seal in a secure location with access limited only to the assigned individual or equipped with other means of preventing potential misuse.

• Use of stored digital images of a person's handwritten signature to sign a document is *not an acceptable practice*. This practice compromises confidence in the authenticity of these signatures when these stored images are not maintained in a secure location, access to which is limited only to the assigned individual, or equipped with other means of preventing potential misuse, and instead are placed in documents and e-mails where they can be easily copied and reused by others. Legally binding, handwritten signatures must be dated at the time of signing, and electronic signatures must include the time/date stamp of signing to record the contemporaneous nature of the signing event.

- The use of hybrid systems is not recommended, but where legacy systems are awaiting replacement, mitigating controls must be in place. The use of shared and generic login credentials must be avoided to ensure that actions documented in electronic records can be attributed to a unique individual. This would apply to the software application level and all applicable network environments where personnel may perform actions (for example, workstation and server operating systems).

- Where such technical controls are not available or feasible, for example, in legacy electronic systems or where login would terminate an application or stop the process running, combinations of paper and electronic records must be used to meet the requirements to attribute actions to the individuals concerned. In such cases, original records generated during GXP activities must be complete and must be maintained throughout the records' retention period in a manner that allows the full reconstruction of the GXP activities.

- A common situation is the existence of legacy equipment with a programmable logic controller (PLC) control that does not allow the individual login of a user. An interim solution is to use a logbook where each individual interacting with the PLC must document in chronological order his/her signature and date as well as a brief explanation of the reason for the interaction.

- A hybrid approach might exceptionally be used to sign electronic records when the system lacks features for electronic signatures, provided adequate security can be maintained. The hybrid approach is likely to be more burdensome than a fully electronic approach; therefore, utilizing electronic signatures, whenever available, is recommended. For example, the execution and attribution of an electronic record by attachment of a handwritten signature may be performed through a simple means that would create a single-page controlled form associated with the written procedures for system use and data review.

    The document must list the electronic data set reviewed and any metadata subject to review and would provide fields for the author, reviewer, and/or approver of the data set to insert a hand-written signature. This paper record with the handwritten signatures must then be securely and traceably linked to the electronic data set, either through procedural means, such as use of detailed archive indexes, or technical means, such as embedding a true-copy scanned image of the signature page into the electronic data set.

Note: It is important to point out that replacement of the kind of hybrid systems described above must be a priority for the company. Regulatory authorities see those hybrid systems as interim measures of control until updated equipment and systems are implemented, allowing the full implementation of electronic data controls.

- A special topic regarding the attributability of data is the use of a *scribe* to record an activity on behalf of another individual. It must be considered only on an exceptional basis and must only take place where:

  - The act of recording places the product or activity at risk (for example, documenting line interventions by aseptic area operators)

  - To accommodate cultural differences or mitigate staff literacy/language limitations (for instance, where an activity is performed by an operator, but witnessed and recorded by a second person)

In these situations, the recording by the second person must be contemporaneous with the task being performed and the records must identify both the person performing the task and the person completing the record. The person performing the observed task must countersign the record wherever possible, although it is accepted that this countersigning step will be retrospective. The process for supervisory (scribe) documentation completion must be described in an approved procedure that must also specify the activities to which the process applies.

3.2 LEGIBLE, TRACEABLE, AND PERMANENT

The terms legible, traceable, and permanent refer to the requirements that data are readable and understandable and allow a clear picture of the sequencing of steps or events in the record so all GXP activities conducted can be fully reconstructed by people reviewing these records at any point during the records' retention period set by the applicable GXP. Table 3.2 depicts the

Table 3.2 Legible, traceable, and permanent records

Legible, traceable, and permanent	
Expectations for paper records	**Expectations for electronic records**
Legible, traceable, and permanent controls for paper records include:	Legible, traceable, and permanent controls for electronic records include:
• Use of permanent, indelible ink • Pencil or erasures are prohibited • Use of single-line cross-outs to record changes with name, date, and reason recorded (this is the paper equivalent to the electronic audit trail) • No use of opaque correction fluid or otherwise obscuring of the record • Controlled issuance of bound, paginated notebooks with sequentially numbered pages (to allow detection of missing or skipped pages) • Controlled issuance of sequentially numbered copies of blank forms (allowing that all issued forms can be accounted for) • Archiving of paper records by independent, designated personnel in secure and controlled paper archives; in GMP settings, this role is normally designated to specific individual(s) in the quality assurance unit • Preservation of paper/ink that fades over time, where their use is unavoidable	• Designing and configuring computer systems and writing procedures, as required, that enforce the saving of electronic data at the time of the activity and before proceeding to the next step of the sequence of events (such as controls that prohibit generation and processing and deletion of data in temporary memory and that instead enforce the committing of the data at the time of the activity to durable memory before moving to the next step in the sequence) • Use of secure, timestamped audit trails that independently record operator actions and attribute actions to the logged-on individual • Configuration settings that restrict access to enhanced security permissions (such as the systems administrator role that can be used to potentially turn off the audit trails or enable overwriting and deletion of data), only to persons independent of those responsible for the content of the electronic records

Table 3.2　Legible, traceable, and permanent records (continued)

Legible, traceable, and permanent	
Expectations for paper records	**Expectations for electronic records**
	• Configuration settings and writing procedures, as required, to disable and prohibit the ability to overwrite data, including prohibiting overwriting of preliminary and intermediate processing of data
	• Strictly controlled configuration and use of data annotation tools in a manner that prevents data in displays and printouts from being obscured
	• Validated backup of electronic records to ensure disaster recovery
	• Validated archiving of electronic records by independent, designated archivist(s) in secure and controlled electronic archives

expectations for legible, traceable, and permanent paper and electronic records.

Potential areas of concern and risk management considerations for legible, traceable, and permanent recording of GXP data

- When computerized systems are used to generate electronic data, it is necessary to be able to associate all changes to data with the people who make those changes, and those changes must be time-stamped and a reason for the change recorded where applicable. This traceability of user actions must be documented via computer-generated audit trails or in other metadata fields or system features that meet these requirements.

- Users must not be able to amend or switch off the audit trails or alternative means of providing traceability of user actions.

- The need for the implementation of appropriate audit trail functionality must be considered for all new computerized systems.

- Where an existing computerized system lacks computer-generated audit trails, personnel may use alternative means such as procedurally controlled use of logbooks, change control, record version control, or other combinations of paper and electronic records to meet GXP regulatory expectations for traceability to document the what, who, when, and why of an action. Procedural controls must include written procedures, training programs, review of records and audits, and self-inspections of the governing processes.

- When archiving of electronic records is used, the process must be done in a controlled manner to preserve the integrity of the records. Electronic archives must be validated, secured, and maintained in a state of control throughout the data life cycle. Electronic records archived manually or automatically must be stored in secure and controlled electronic archives, accessible only by independent, designated archivists or by their approved delegates.

- Appropriate separation of duties must be established so users who may have a conflict of interest are not granted enhanced security access permissions at any system level, such as operating system, application, and database.

- Highly privileged systems administrator accounts must be reserved for designated technical personnel, typically IT personnel, who are fully independent of the personnel responsible for the content of the records (laboratory analysts, laboratory management, clinical investigators, study directors, production operators, or production management), as these types of accounts may include the ability to change settings to overwrite, rename, delete, and move data, change time/date settings, disable audit trails, and perform other system maintenance functions that turn off good data and record management controls for legible and traceable electronic data. Where it is not feasible to assign these independent security roles, other control strategies must be used to reduce data validity risks.

- It is particularly important that individuals with enhanced access permissions understand the impact of any changes they make using these privileges. Personnel with enhanced access must therefore also be trained in data integrity principles.

3.3 CONTEMPORANEOUS

Contemporaneous data are data recorded at the time they are generated or observed. Table 3.3 depicts the expectations for contemporaneous paper and electronic records.

Potential areas of concern and risk management considerations for contemporaneous recording of GXP data

- Training programs in good documentation practices must emphasize that it is unacceptable to record data first in unofficial documentation (for example, on scrap paper) and later transfer the data to official documentation (for example, production records or laboratory notebook). Instead, original data must be recorded directly in official records, such as approved analytical worksheets, immediately at the time of the GXP activity.

- Training programs must emphasize that it is unacceptable to back-date or forward date a record. Instead, the date recorded must be the actual date (and time, if required) of the data entry.

- Late entries must be indicated as such with both the date of the activity and the date of the entry being recorded. See Section 2.3.5.

- If a person makes mistakes on a paper document, he or she must make single-line corrections, sign and date them, provide reasons for the changes, and retain this record in the record set.

- If users of standalone computerized systems are provided with full administrator rights to the workstation operating systems on which the original electronic records are stored, this may inappropriately grant permission to users to rename, copy or delete files stored on the local system, and change the time/date stamp. For this reason, validation of the standalone computerized system must ensure proper security restrictions to protect time/date settings and ensure data integrity in all computing environments, including the workstation operating system, the software application, and any other applicable network environments.

Table 3.3 Contemporaneous records

Contemporaneous	
Expectations for paper records	**Expectations for electronic records**
Contemporaneous recording of actions in paper records must occur, as appropriate, through use of:	Contemporaneous recording of actions in electronic records must occur, as appropriate, through use of:
• Written procedures, training, review, audit, and self-inspection controls that ensure personnel record data entries and information at the time of the activity directly in official controlled documents (for example, laboratory notebooks, production records, CRFs, and so on)	• Configuration settings, procedures, and controls that ensure data recorded in temporary memory are committed to durable media upon completion of the step or event and before proceeding to the next step or event in order to ensure the permanent recording of the step or event at the time it is conducted
• Procedures requiring that activities be recorded in paper records with the date of the activity (and time as well, if it is a time-sensitive activity)	• Secure system time/date stamps that cannot be altered by personnel
• Appropriate record design, which encourages good documentation practices	• Procedures and maintenance programs that ensure time/date stamps are synchronized across the GXP operations
• Ensuring the availability of blank forms and documents in which the activities must be recorded	• Controls that allow for the determination of the timing of one activity relative to another (time zone controls)
• Recording of the date and time of activities using synchronized time sources (facility and computerized system clocks) that cannot be changed by unauthorized personnel; where possible, data and time recording of manual activities (for example, weighing) must be done automatically	• Availability of the system to the user at the time of the activity

3.4 ORIGINAL

Original data include the first or source capture of data or information and all subsequent data required to fully reconstruct the conduct of the GXP activity. The GXP requirements for original data include the following:

- Original data must be reviewed

- Original data and/or true and verified copies that preserve the content and meaning of the original data must be retained

- As such, original records must be complete, enduring, and readily retrievable and readable throughout the records' retention period

Examples of original data include:

a. Original electronic data and metadata in standalone computerized laboratory instrument systems:

   - Ultraviolet/visible spectrophotometry (UV/Vis)

   - Fourier-transform infrared spectroscopy (FT-IR)

   - Electrocardiograms (ECGs)

   - Liquid chromatography-tandem mass spectrometry (LC/MS/MS)

   - Hematology and chemistry analyzers

b. Original electronic data and metadata in automated production systems:

   - Automated filter integrity testers

   - Supervisory control and data acquisition (SCADA)

   - Distributed control systems (DCSs)

c. Original electronic data and metadata in network database systems:

   - Laboratory information management systems (LIMSs)

   - Enterprise resource planning (ERP)

   - Manufacturing execution systems (MES)

   - Electronic case report form/electronic data capture (eCRF/EDC)

   - Toxicology databases

   - Investigation, deviation, and corrective and preventive action (CAPA) databases

d. Handwritten sample preparation information in paper notebooks

e. Printed recordings of balance readings

f. Electronic health records

g. Paper production records

Table 3.4 depicts the expectations for the review process of original paper and electronic records.

Potential areas of concern and risk management considerations for review of original records

- Data integrity risks may occur when people choose to rely solely upon paper printouts or PDF reports from computerized systems without meeting applicable regulatory expectations for original records. Original records must be reviewed, and this includes electronic records. If the reviewer only reviews the subset of data provided as a printout or PDF, integrity problems may go undetected.

- Systems typically include many metadata fields and audit trails. It is expected that during validation of the system, the organization will establish, based upon a documented and justified risk assessment, the frequency, roles and responsibilities, and approach used to review the various types of meaningful metadata, such as audit trails. For example, under some circumstances, an organization may justify periodic review of audit trails that track system maintenance activities, whereas audit trails that track changes to critical GXP data with a direct impact on patient safety or product quality would be expected to be reviewed each and every time the associated data set is being reviewed and approved, and prior to decision making.

- Certain aspects of defining the audit trail review process (such as frequency) may be initiated during validation and then adjusted over time during the system life cycle, based upon risk reviews and to ensure continual improvement.

- A risk-based approach to reviewing data requires process understanding and knowledge of the key quality risks in the given process that may impact patients, products, compliance, and the overall accuracy, consistency, and reliability of GXP decision making. When original records are electronic, a risk-based approach to reviewing original electronic data also requires an understanding of the computerized system, data, metadata, and data flows.

Table 3.4   Review of original records

Review of original records	
Expectations for paper records	**Expectations for electronic records**
Controls for review of original paper records include:	Controls for review of original electronic records include:
• Written procedures, training, review, and audit and self-inspection controls to ensure that personnel conduct an adequate review and approval of original paper records, including those used to record the contemporaneous capture of information	• Written procedures, training, review and audit and self-inspection controls to ensure personnel conduct an adequate review and approval of original electronic records, including human-readable source records of electronic data
• Data review procedures describing review of relevant metadata. For example, written procedures for review must require that personnel evaluate changes made to original information on paper records (such as changes documented in cross-out or data correction) to ensure these changes are appropriately documented and justified with substantiating evidence and investigated when required.	• Data review procedures describing review of original electronic data and relevant metadata. For example, written procedures for review must require that personnel evaluate changes made to original information in electronic records (such as changes documented in audit trails or history fields or found in other meaningful metadata) to ensure these changes are appropriately documented and justified with substantiating evidence and investigated when required.
• Documentation of data review. For paper records, this is typically indicated by signing the paper records that have been reviewed. Where record approval is a separate process, this must also be similarly signed. Written procedures for data review must clarify the meaning of the review and approval signatures to ensure	• Documentation of data review. For electronic records, this is typically indicated by electronically signing the electronic data set that has been reviewed and approved. Written procedures for data review must clarify the meaning of the review and

Table 3.4 Review of original records (continued)

Review of original records	
Expectations for paper records	**Expectations for electronic records**
that the people concerned understand their responsibility as reviewers and approvers to ensure the integrity, accuracy, consistency, and compliance with established standards of the paper records subject to review and approval. • A procedure describing the actions to be taken if data review identifies an error or omission. This procedure must enable data corrections or clarifications to be made in a GXP-compliant manner, providing visibility of the original record and audit-trailed traceability of the correction, using ALCOA principles.	approval signatures to ensure the personnel concerned understand their responsibility as reviewers and approvers to assure the integrity, accuracy, consistency, and compliance with established standards of the electronic data and metadata subject to review and approval. • A procedure describing the actions to be taken if data review identifies an error or omission. This procedure must enable data corrections or clarifications to be made in a GXP-compliant manner, providing visibility of the original record and audit-trailed traceability of the correction, using ALCOA principles.

- When determining a risk-based approach to reviewing audit trails in GXP computerized systems, it is important to note that some software developers may design mechanisms for tracking user actions related to the most critical GXP data using metadata features and may not have named these "audit trails"—but may instead have used the naming convention "audit trail" to track other computer system and file maintenance activities. The risk-based review of electronic data and metadata, such as audit trails, requires an understanding of the system and the scientific process governing the data life cycle so the meaningful metadata are subject to review, regardless of the naming conventions used by the software developer.

- Systems may be designed to facilitate audit trail review by various means. One example is the system design may permit audit trails to be reviewed as a list of relevant data or by a validated exception reporting process.

- Written procedures for data review must define the frequency, roles, responsibilities, and approaches to review of meaningful metadata, such as audit trails. These procedures must also describe how aberrant data are to be handled if found during the review. Personnel who conduct such reviews must have adequate and appropriate training in the review process as well as in the software systems containing the data subject to review. The company must make the necessary provisions for personnel reviewing the data to access the system(s) containing the electronic data and metadata.

- Quality assurance must also review a sample of relevant audit trails, raw data, and metadata as part of self-inspection to ensure ongoing compliance with the data governance policy and procedures. Any significant variation from expected outcomes must be fully recorded and investigated.

- In the hybrid approach, which should be an interim approach as previously mentioned, paper printouts of original electronic records from computerized systems may be useful as summary reports if the requirements for original electronic records are also met. To rely upon these printed summaries of results for future decision making, a second person would have to review the original electronic data and any relevant metadata such as audit trails, to verify that the printed summary is representative of all results. This verification would then be documented, and the printout could be used for subsequent decision making.

- The GXP organization may choose a fully electronic approach to allow more efficient, streamlined record review and record retention. This would require authenticated and secure electronic signatures to be implemented for signing records where required. This, in turn, would require preservation of the original electronic records, or true copy, as well as the necessary software and hardware or other suitable reader equipment to view the records during the records' retention period.

- System design and the manner of data capture can significantly influence the ease with which data consistency can be ensured. For example, and where applicable, programmed edit checks or features such as drop-down lists, check boxes, or branching of questions or data fields based on entries are useful in improving data consistency.

- Data and their metadata must be maintained in such a way that they are available for review by authorized individuals, and in a format that is suitable for review for as long as the data retention requirements apply. It is desirable that the data must be maintained and available in the original system in which they were generated for the longest possible period of time. When the original system is retired or decommissioned, migration of the data to other systems or other means of preserving the data must be used in a manner that preserves the context and meaning of the data, allowing the relevant steps to be reconstructed. Checks of accessibility to archived data, irrespective of format, and including relevant metadata, must be undertaken to confirm the data are enduring and continue to be available, readable, and understandable by a human being.

3.4.1 Retention of original records or true copies

Table 3.5 depicts the expectations for the retention of original or true copies of paper and electronic records.

As an example of regulatory requirements for retention of records, the FDA's Sec. §§ 211.180 under general requirement for records establishes that:

(c) All records required under this part, or copies of such records, shall be readily available for authorized inspection during the retention period at the establishment where the activities described in such records occurred. These records or copies thereof shall be subject to photocopying or other means of reproduction as part of such inspection. Records that can be immediately retrieved from another location by computer or other electronic means shall be considered as meeting the requirements of this paragraph.

(d) Records required under this part may be retained either as original records or as true copies such as photocopies, microfilm, microfiche, or other accurate reproductions of the original records. Where reduction techniques, such as microfilming, are used, suitable reader and photocopying equipment shall be readily available.

Potential areas of concern and risk management considerations for retention of original records or true copies

- Data and document retention arrangements must ensure the protection of records from deliberate or inadvertent alteration or loss.

Table 3.5   Retention of original records or true copies

Retention of original records or true copies	
Expectations for paper records	**Expectations for electronic records**
Controls for retention of original paper records or true copies of original paper records include:	Controls for retention of original electronic records or true copies of original electronic records include:
• Controlled and secure storage areas, including archives, for paper records	• Routine backup copies of original electronic records stored in another location as a safeguard in case of disaster that causes loss of the original electronic records
• A designated paper archivist(s) who is independent of GXP operations is required by GLP guidelines; in other GXPs, the roles and responsibilities for archiving GXP records must be defined and monitored (and must normally be the responsibility of the quality assurance function or an independent documentation control unit)	• Controlled and secure storage areas, including archives, for electronic records
	• A designated electronic archivist(s) such as is required in GLP guidelines who is independent of GXP operations (the designated personnel must be suitably qualified and have relevant experience and appropriate training to perform their duties)
• Indexing of records to permit ready retrieval	• Indexing of records to permit ready retrieval
• Periodic tests at appropriate intervals based upon risk assessment to verify the ability to retrieve archived paper or static format records	• Periodic tests to verify the ability to retrieve archived electronic data from storage locations. The ability to retrieve archived electronic data from storage locations must be tested during the validation of the electronic archive. After validation, the ability to retrieve archived electronic data from the storage locations must be periodically reconfirmed, including retrieval from third-party storage.
• The provision of suitable reader equipment when required, such as microfiche or microfilm readers if original paper records are copied as true copies to microfilm or microfiche for archiving	

Table 3.5   Retention of original records or true copies (continued)

Retention of original records or true copies

Expectations for paper records	Expectations for electronic records

• Written procedures, training, review, audit, and self-inspection controls of processes defining conversion, as needed, of an original paper record to true copy must include the following steps:
 	
  – A copy is made of the original paper record, preserving the original record format, the static format, as required (for example, photocopy or scan)
 	
  – The copy must be compared with the original record to determine if the copy preserves the entire content and meaning of the original record, that metadata are included, and that no data are missing in the copy. The way the record format is preserved is important for record meaning if the copy is to meet the requirements of a true copy of the original paper record(s).
 	
  – The verifier documents the verification in a manner securely linked to the copy/copies indicating it is a true copy, or provides equivalent certification
	• The provision of suitable reader equipment, such as software, operating systems, and virtualized environments, to view the archived electronic data when required
	
	• Written procedures, training, review, audit, and self-inspection controls of processes defining conversion, as needed, of original electronic records to true copy must include the following steps:
	
	  – A copy is made of the original electronic data set, preserving the original record format, the dynamic format, as required (archival copy of the entire set of electronic data and metadata made using a validated backup process)
	
	  – A second verifier or technical verification process (such as use of technical hash) to confirm successful backup, whereby a comparison is made of the electronic archival copy with the original electronic data set to confirm the copy preserves the entire content and meaning of the original record. (All of the data and metadata are included,

Table 3.5   Retention of original records or true copies (*continued*)

Retention of original records or true copies

Expectations for paper records	Expectations for electronic records
	and no data are missing in the copy. Any dynamic record format that is important for record meaning and interpretation is preserved, and the file was not corrupted during the execution of the validated backup process.)
	− If the copy meets the requirements as a true copy of the original, then the verifier or technical verification process must document the verification in a manner that is securely linked to the copy/copies, certifying that it is a true copy

Secure controls must be in place to ensure the data integrity of the record throughout the retention period. Archival processes must be defined in written procedures and validated where appropriate. Regulated companies must consider any risk associated with the destruction of original records, such as legal or regulatory risks.

• Data collected or recorded (manually and/or by recording instruments or computerized systems) during a process or procedure must show that all the defined and required steps have been taken and that the quantity and quality of the output are as expected and must enable the complete history of the process or material to be traced and be retained in a comprehensible and accessible form. That is, original records and/or true copies must be complete, consistent, and enduring.

• A true copy of original records may be retained in lieu of the original records only if the copy has been compared to the original records and verified to contain the entire content and meaning of the original records, including applicable metadata and audit trails. Where manual transcriptions occur, these must be verified by a second person or validated system.

- If true copies of original paper records are made by scanning the original paper and conversion to an electronic image, such as a PDF, then additional measures to protect the electronic image from further alteration are required (for example, storage in a secure network location with access limited to electronic archivist personnel only, and measures taken to control potential use of annotation tools or other means of preventing further alteration of the copy).

- Consideration must be given to preservation where necessary of the full content and meaning of original hand-signed paper records, especially when the handwritten signature is an important aspect of the overall integrity and reliability of the record and in accordance with the value of the record over time. For example, in a clinical trial it may be important to preserve original hand-signed informed consent records throughout the useful life of this record as an essential aspect of the trial and related application integrity.

- True copies of electronic records must preserve the dynamic format of the original electronic data, as this is essential to preserving the meaning of the original electronic data, especially in situations where the old software or equipment is retired. For example, the original dynamic electronic spectral files created by instruments such as FT-IR, UV/Vis, chromatography systems, and others can be reprocessed, but a PDF or printout is fixed or static, and the ability to expand baselines, view the full spectrum, reprocess, and interact dynamically with the data set would be lost in the PDF or printout.

- As another example, preserving the dynamic format of clinical study data captured in an eCRF system allows searching and querying of data, whereas a PDF of the eCRF data, even if it includes a PDF of audit trails, would lose this aspect of the content and meaning of the original eCRF data. Clinical investigators must have access to original records throughout the study and the records' retention period in a manner that preserves the full content and meaning of the source information. It may be decided to maintain complete copies of electronic data as well as PDF/printed summaries of the electronic data in the archives to mitigate risks of a complete loss of ability to readily view the data in case the software and hardware is retired. However, under these circumstances, especially for data that support critical decision making, even if PDF/printed summaries are maintained, the complete copies of electronic data must continue to be maintained throughout the records' retention period to allow for investigations that may be necessary under unexpected circumstances, such as application integrity investigations.

- Preserving the original electronic data in electronic form is also important because data in a dynamic format facilitate usability of the data for subsequent processes. For example, having temperature logger data maintained electronically facilitates subsequent tracking, trending, and monitoring of temperatures in statistical process control charts.

- In addition to the option of creating true copies of original electronic data as verified backup copies that are then secured in electronic archives, another option for creating a true copy of original electronic data would be to migrate the original electronic data from one system to another and to verify and document that the validated data migration process preserved the entire content, including all meaningful metadata, as well as the meaning of the original electronic data.

- Electronic signature information must be retained as part of the original electronic record. This must remain linked to the record and be readable throughout the retention period, regardless of the system used for archiving the records.

Can electronic copies be used as accurate reproductions of paper or electronic records? Electronic copies can be used as true copies of paper or electronic records, provided the copies preserve the content and meaning of the original data, which includes associated metadata and the static or dynamic nature of the original records.

True copies of dynamic electronic records may be made and maintained in the format of the original records or in a compatible format, provided that the content and meaning of the original records are preserved and that a suitable reader and copying equipment (for example, software and hardware, including media readers) are readily available.

Is it acceptable to retain paper printouts or static records instead of original electronic records from standalone computerized laboratory instruments, such as an FT-IR instrument? A paper printout or static record may satisfy retention requirements if it is a complete copy of the original record. For example, pH meters and balances may create a paper printout or static image during data acquisition as the original record. In this case, the paper printout or static image created during acquisition, or a true copy, must be retained.

However, electronic records from certain types of laboratory instruments are dynamic records, and a printout or a static record does not preserve the dynamic format that is part of the complete original record. For example, the spectral file created by FT-IR can be reprocessed, but a static record or printout is fixed, which would not satisfy cGMP requirements to retain original

---

Table 3.6   Accuracy of data

Accuracy of data for paper and electronic records

Controls that assure the accuracy of data in paper records and electronic records include, among others, the following:

- Qualification, calibration, and maintenance of equipment, such as balances and pH meters, that generates printouts

- Validation of computerized systems that generate, process, maintain, distribute, or archive electronic records

- Systems must be validated to ensure their integrity while transmitting between/among computerized systems

- Validation of analytical methods

- Validation of production processes

- Review of GXP records

- Investigation of deviations and doubtful and out-of-specification results

- Verification by second person that significant/critical data being recorded is accurate

---

records or true copies. Also, if the full spectrum is not displayed, contaminants may be excluded. Control strategies must ensure that original laboratory records, including paper and electronic records, are subject to second-person review to make certain that all test results are appropriately reported.

3.5 ACCURATE

The term "accurate" means data are correct, truthful, complete, valid, and reliable. For both paper and electronic records, achieving the goal of accurate data requires adequate procedures, processes, systems, and controls that comprise the quality management system. The quality management system must be appropriate to the scope of its activities and risk based. Table 3.6 depicts the accuracy of data expectations for paper and electronic records.

Potential areas of concern and risk management considerations for ensuring accurate GXP records

- The entry of critical data into a paper record or into a computer by an authorized person requires an additional check on the accuracy of the data entered manually. This check may be done by independent verification by a second authorized person or by validated electronic means. For example, to detect and manage risks associated with critical data, procedures would require verification by a second person (or by validated electronic means) of:

– Weighing and addition of components

– Calculation of yield for pharmaceutical production

– Calculation formulas entered into spreadsheets

– Master data entered into LIMSs such as fields for specification ranges used to flag out-of-specification values on the certificate of analysis

– Any other significant or critical data, as appropriate

• In addition, once verified, these critical data fields must be locked to prevent further modification, when feasible and appropriate, and only modified through a formal change control process.

• Where used, standard dictionaries, thesauruses, and tables (for example, units and scales) must be controlled.

• The process of data transfer between systems must be validated.

• The migration of data into and export from systems requires specific planned testing and control.

• Time may not be critical for all activities. When the activity is time critical, printed records must display the time/date stamp. For example, to ensure the accuracy of sample weights recorded on a paper printout from the balance, the balance would be appropriately calibrated before use and properly maintained. In addition, synchronizing and locking the metadata settings on the balance for the time/date settings would ensure accurate recordings of time/date on the balance printout.

4

Regulatory Expectations

4.1 HISTORICAL PERSPECTIVE

Data integrity and data management problems within medical product manufacturing companies are not new. The current high-intensity focus by worldwide regulatory authorities represents the evolution over the past 40 years. In the case of the United States, since the approval of the 21 CFR § 211 regulation for cGMP for finished pharmaceuticals, GDocPs and the requirement for record keeping were an integral part of this regulation.

Going back a few years, in the United States, the Food, Drug, and Cosmetic Act of 1938 required the safety of new drugs be shown prior to their marketing. In 1962, the Kefauver-Harris amendment to this act, also known as the "Drug Efficacy Amendment," was passed, introducing the requirement for drug manufacturers to provide proof of the effectiveness and safety of their drugs before approval. Before that, U.S. drug companies only had to show their new products were safe. After the passage of the amendment, an FDA New Drug Application (NDA) would have to show that a new drug was both safe and effective.

The amendment was a response to the thalidomide tragedy, in which thousands of children were born in the United Kingdom and other countries with birth defects because of their mothers taking thalidomide for morning sickness during pregnancy. It was precisely those incidents with thalidomide in the 1950s and 1960s that led to the creation of the UK Committee on Safety of Drugs in 1963.

Regarding medical device regulation in the United States, although they were first brought under FDA control in 1938, it was the medical device amendments of 1976 to the Food, Drug, and Cosmetic Act of 1938 that established the current regulatory landscape. The passing of those medical device amendments was aided by several widespread incidents with medical devices, including an intrauterine device that injured more than 900,000 women in the United States.[1]

In Europe, the Council of the European Economic Community Directive 765/65/EEC of January 1965 and subsequent amendments established the regulatory framework for European member states.

In Japan, the Fund for Adverse Drug Reactions Suffering Relief was established in October 1979 and in 1993 became the Organization for Pharmaceutical Safety and Research to perform the generic drug reviews.

All of those national or regional regulations and laws, as well as guidance prepared by the WHO, embraced the topic of good documentation practices and record keeping.

Historically, manufacturing and quality control records as well as clinical data were paper based and thus subject to the integrity of the individuals responsible for documenting and checking the data entries. The computer age gradually introduced electronic data, which, when properly managed, increased the control and integrity of data.

Data may be generated from a variety of sources, including toxicology studies, nonclinical and clinical studies, manufacturing operations, laboratory testing, and so on. The data may support regulatory submissions and/or required documentation for cGMP activities.

Although data integrity problems have occurred for a long time, now they are at the forefront of very visible enforcement actions. For example, in August 2015, the European Union banned the marketing of about 700 Indian-made generic drugs for alleged manipulation of clinical trials data. The largest-ever EU-wide suspension of sales and distribution of generic drugs ordered by the European Commission was applicable to all 28 member nations.[2]

Between 2015 and 2016, six major international regulatory authorities published guidance documents addressing data management and data integrity. Two of these, the draft guidance published by the U.S. FDA in April 2016 (the final guidance version was published December 2018) and the guidance posted by the EMA in August 2016, take a question-and-answer approach. The guidance from the UK's MHRA, the China Food and Drug Administration (CFDA), the PIC/S, and the WHO take a more standard narrative approach to their regulatory guidance. However, all six guidance documents are very similar in their overall expectations.

---

[1] Hicks, Karen M. (1994). *Surviving the Dalcon Shield IUD: Women v. The Pharmaceutical Industry*. New York: Teachers College Press.

[2] http://www.financialexpress.com/industry/european-union-bans-700-generic-drugs -for-manipulation-of-trials-by-gvk-biosciences/107418/. Accessed December 24, 2018.

4.2 U.S. FDA

The first significant data integrity scandal in the United States happened during the 1970s where an investigation revealed G. D. Searle Company submitted fraudulent animal data as part of applications submitted to the FDA. The information was covered in *The New York Times* on April 8, 1976, with the headline: "F.D.A. Urges Grand Jury Study of G. D. Searle's Drug Reports."[3]

The Food and Drug Administration has recommended to the Justice Department that a grand jury be convened in Illinois to investigate charges that a major drug firm, G.D. Searle & Company, has falsified data and reports submitted in connection with new drug applications.

Charges that the company was giving the Government false information were made last summer by a medical officer of the drug agency. Since these disclosures the drug agency has mobilized to investigate in detail some 16 studies conducted by or for the drug company in its applications for drug approvals.

Because the drug agency does not have subpoena power, it has asked for the grand jury investigation to obtain additional facts in the case, an officer of the agency indicated tonight.

Testimony concerning the agency's action is to be given here tomorrow by Dr. Alexander M. Schmidt, Commissioner of Food and Drugs, at a Senate subcommittee hearing. The testimony is expected to say that animal studies related to several drugs were involved in the F.D.A. task force's investigation, but that safety of the drugs on the market was not called into question by the task force findings. Before a drug is approved for marketing tests in humans as well as animals are required. It is understood that the case against G. D. Searle and Company is related to animal tests only.

Among the drugs under scrutiny were Aldactone, a diuretic designed to help the body remove excess fluid, and Flagyl, used against vaginal infections. In both cases, the drug agency plans to require that the labeling of the drug changed, presumably in the light of some of the findings that have been made during the investigation. Also investigated were studies done for the company in support of applications to market an artificial sweetener called Aspartame.

---

[3] https://www.nytimes.com/1976/04/08/archives/fda-urges-grand-jury-study-of-gd
-searles-drug-reports.html. Accessed December 24, 2018.

The task force analysis of the studies submitted by Searle was described as extremely thorough and involved talking to animal handlers and others involved in the work, reviewing the raw data and all but recreating the studies. Altogether several million items of information were said to have been analyzed.

The investigation reportedly revealed practices such as the withholding of information and the deliberate manipulation of data to give impressions favorable to the drugs under study. It is known that Dr. Schmidt believes there is a widespread problem of quality of animal research related to drug approvals in the drug industry. An investigation much more widespread than that involving the Illinois company is expected.

The FDA investigation into those toxicological animal data integrity issue led to the GLP regulations that were put in place in 1979.

The second scandal was the so-called "generics scandal" of the 1980s, which raised the issue of falsified data submitted to the FDA in support of marketing applications. Numerous generic drug manufacturers submitted fraudulent data as part of their Abbreviated New Drug Application (ANDA).

Thereafter, numerous changes were implemented by the FDA to improve data integrity compliance and toughen the penalties for such egregious acts. The changes included updating the preapproval inspection (PAI) program to change the focus on the evaluation of raw laboratory data included in the regulatory application and evaluate whether the site was capable of manufacture as described in the application.

Another significant change was the implementation of the application integrity policy (AIP), which describes the agency's approach regarding the review of applications that may be affected by wrongful acts that raise significant questions regarding data reliability. A list of companies subject to the AIP is available on the FDA website.[4] The FDA published this policy, formally titled "Fraud, Untrue Statements of Material Facts, Bribery, and Illegal Gratuities; Final Policy," in the *Federal Register* on September 10, 1991, and in the Compliance Policy Guide (CPG) Sec. 120.100, "Fraud, Untrue Statements of Material Facts, Bribery, and Illegal Gratuities," and the Generic Drug Enforcement Act (GDEA) of 1992.

GDEA included provisions for debarment of corporations and individuals, authority to deny or withdraw product approval, the suspension of product distribution, agency hearings, judicial review of GDEA decisions, civil penalties, certifications, and effects on other laws.

---

[4]   https://www.fda.gov/ICECI/EnforcementActions/ApplicationIntegrityPolicy/ucm 134453.htm. Accessed December 26, 2018.

The following are details of the "generic scandal" as narrated by the FDA:[5]

The United States Congress began an investigation of wrongful acts involving some manufacturers of generic drugs and some employees of the FDA during July 1988. As a result of those investigations and investigations conducted by FDA, four FDA employees were found to have accepted illegal gratuities from generic drug companies, and to date, eleven generic drug companies were found to have falsified data submitted in premarket applications to FDA.

In FDA's investigations, which began as inquiries into illegal gratuities and questionable data submissions, the agency discovered broad patterns and practices of fraud in the applicants' abbreviated new drug applications. The discovery of this extensive pattern of fraudulent data submissions prompted FDA to develop a program:

1) to ensure validity of data submissions called into question by the agency's discovery of wrongful acts such as fraud, untrue statements of material fact, bribery, and illegal gratuities, and;

2) to withdraw approval of, or refuse to approve, applications containing fraudulent data.

Validity Assessment—Actions on the part of an applicant to subvert the integrity of an FDA review process through acts such as submitting fraudulent applications, making untrue statements of material facts, or giving or promising bribes or illegal gratuities may call into question the integrity of some or all of the applicant's submissions to the agency. In such cases, FDA will conduct an investigation to identify all instances of wrongful acts and to determine the extent to which the wrongful acts may have affected approved or pending applications. The scope of FDA's investigation will be determined based on the nature of the offense and will focus on the reliability of the applicant's research and manufacturing data. If the wrongful acts have raised a significant question regarding reliability of data in some or all of the applicant's pending applications, FDA ordinarily will conduct validity assessments of those applications.

FDA generally intends to defer substantive scientific review of the data in a pending application undergoing a validity assessment until the assessment is complete and questions regarding reli-

---

[5] https://www.fda.gov/ICECI/ComplianceManuals/CompliancePolicyGuidanceManual /ucm073837.htm. Accessed December 26, 2018.

ability of the data are resolved. To approve an application, FDA generally must determine that the applicant is capable of producing a safe and, for some types of applications, an effective or functional product based on, among other things, testing and other data provided by the applicant and the adequacy of the applicant's manufacturing processes and controls. The principle basis for this determination is the data in the application; therefore, the reliability of data is of critical importance.

If the agency determines the criteria for approval cannot be met because of unresolved questions regarding reliability of data, the agency will not approve the application.

When FDA finds, based on fraudulent data in an application, that the data in the application are unreliable, the agency intends ordinarily to exercise its authority, under applicable statutes and regulations, to refuse to approve the application (in the case of a pending application) or to proceed to withdraw approval (in the case of an approved application), regardless of whether the applicant attempts to replace the unreliable data with a new submission in the form of an amendment or supplement. Thus, if the applicant wishes to replace the false data with a new submission, the new submission must be in the form of a new application. The new application must identify the parts of the original application that were found to be false. The truthfulness and accuracy of the new application must be certified by the president, chief executive officer, or other official most responsible for the applicant's operations.

FDA also may seek recalls of marketed products and may request new testing of critical products. For drugs, for example, retesting may be requested for products that are difficult to manufacture or that have narrow therapeutic ranges. FDA may pursue other actions, including seizure, injunction, civil penalties, and criminal prosecution, under the act or other applicable laws, as necessary and appropriate.

Corrective Actions—The corrective actions an applicant will be expected to take will depend upon the facts and circumstances of each case, the nature of the wrongful acts, the nature of the data under consideration, and the requirements of the particular review process.

Applicants who engage in wrongful acts ordinarily will need to take the following corrective actions to establish the reliability of data submitted to FDA in support of pending applications and to support the integrity of products on the market:

1. Cooperate fully with FDA and other Federal investigations to determine the cause and scope of any wrongful acts and to assess the effects of the acts on the safety, effectiveness, or quality of products.

2. Identify all individuals who were or may have been associated with or involved in the wrongful acts and ensure that they are removed from any substantive authority on matters under the jurisdiction of FDA.

3. Conduct a credible internal review designed to identify all instances of wrongful acts associated with applications submitted to FDA, including any discrepancies between manufacturing conditions identified in approved applications and manufacturing conditions during actual production. The internal review is intended to supplement FDA's ongoing, comprehensive investigation to identify all instances of wrongful acts. The internal review must involve an outside consultant or a team of consultants who are qualified by training and experience to conduct such a review. All oral or written reports related to the review that are provided by the consultant to the applicant must be made available simultaneously to FDA for independent verification.

4. Commit, in writing, to developing and implementing a corrective action operating plan to assure the safety, effectiveness, and quality of their products. This commitment ordinarily will be in the form of a consent decree or agreement, signed by the president, chief executive officer, or other official most responsible for the applicant's operations, and submitted to FDA. The corrective action operating plan will, as appropriate, address procedures and controls to preclude future instances of wrongful acts and noncompliance with regulatory requirements for approved applications, as well as procedures and controls to preclude any recurrences of other violations which may have been found (for example, a comprehensive ethics program).

FDA intends to reinspect the applicant to determine that the internal review has been satisfactorily completed and that the applicant's written corrective action operating plan has been satisfactorily implemented. Such inspections must disclose positive evidence (e.g., effective management controls, standard operating procedures, and corroborating documentation) that the applicant's data are reliable and that the applicant can be expected to manufacture products in compliance with current good manufacturing practices and application requirements. In addition, FDA may request an applicant to commit in writing to retest any product (including, in the case of drugs, bioequivalence and bioavailability retesting), as FDA deems appropriate. An applicant also may be requested under existing regulatory procedures to recall products affected by the wrongful acts, or otherwise lacking adequate assurance of safety, effectiveness, or quality.

In parallel, the FDA recognized the increased reliance on computerized systems within the medical product manufacturing industry. The FDA first published 21 CFR Part 11, the final rule on electronic records and electronic signatures in 1997. In 2003, the FDA published "Guidance for Industry, Part 11, Electronic Records; Electronic Signatures—Scope and Application"[6] to clarify the interpretation and enforcement of 1997 requirements.

After the turn of the century, the FDA toughened the enforcement of good documentation practices and data integrity requirements, resulting in a string of enforcement actions (including import alert, warning letters, and consent decrees) lasting up to today. Some of most egregious milestones of those first years are described in Section 5.4. Section 5.5 details statistics and examples of recent enforcements (last five years, from 2013 to 2017).

4.2.1 FDA's guidance for industry: "Data Integrity and Compliance with cGMP—Questions and Answers"

The purpose of this guidance, published in December 2018 is to clarify the role of data integrity in cGMP for drugs, as required in 21 CFR parts § 210, § 211, and § 212.[7] Part 210 covers *cGMP Practice in Manufacturing, Processing, Packing, or Holding of Drugs; General*; part § 211 covers *cGMP for Finished Pharmaceuticals*; and part 212 covers *cGMP for Positron Emission Tomography (PET) Drugs*. As the guidance explains in its introduction, all citations to parts 211 and 212 in the guidance pertains to finished pharmaceuticals and PET drugs, but these requirements are also consistent with FDA guidance on cGMP for active pharmaceutical ingredients with respect to data integrity. This guidance, originally published as a draft guidance

---

[6]   https://www.fda.gov/downloads/RegulatoryInformation/Guidances/ucm125125 .PDF. Accessed December 29, 2018.

[7]   https://www.fda.gov/downloads/drugs/guidances/ucm495891.pdf. Accessed December 25, 2018.

in April 2016, provides the agency's current thinking on the creation and handling of data in accordance with cGMP requirements.

This guidance provides a list of current data integrity problems and how they relate to the cGMP requirements in regulations. Also, it clarifies several terms in the FDA's regulations (for example, metadata, audit trail, static and dynamic records, backup files, and system in computer or related systems). The guidance is not a comprehensive list of data controls or a "how-to" guidance.

The FDA expects that all data be reliable and accurate. cGMP regulations and guidance allow for flexible and risk-based strategies to prevent and detect data integrity issues. Firms must implement meaningful and effective strategies to manage their data integrity risks based upon their process understanding and knowledge management of technologies and business models.

Requirements with respect to data integrity in parts 211 and 212 include, among other things:

- § 211.68 requiring that "backup data are exact and complete" and "secure from alteration, inadvertent erasures, or loss" and that "output from the computer . . . be checked for accuracy"

- § 212.110(b) requiring that data be "stored to prevent deterioration or loss"

- §§ 211.100 and 211.160 requiring that certain activities be "documented at the time of performance" and that laboratory controls be "scientifically sound"

- § 211.180 requiring that records be retained as "original records," "true copies," or other "accurate reproductions of the original records"

- §§ 211.188, 211.194, and 212.60(g) requiring "complete information," "complete data derived from all tests," "complete record of all data," and "complete records of all tests performed"

- §§ 211.22, 211.192, and 211.194(a) requiring that production and control records be "reviewed" and that laboratory records be "reviewed for accuracy, completeness, and compliance with established standards"

- §§ 211.182, 211.186(a), 211.188(b)(11), and 211,194(a)(8) requiring that records be "checked," "verified," or "reviewed"

Table 4.1 depicts the correspondence between existing regulatory requirements and data integrity expectations (ALCOA).

Table 4.1   ALCOA principles and requirements in FDA's 21CFR §§ 211 and 212

ALCOA principle	21 CFR §§ 211 and 212
Attributable	§§ 211.101(d), § 211.122, § 211.186, § 211.188(b)(11), and 212.50(c)(10)
Legible	§§ 211.180(e) and 212.110(b)
Contemporaneous	§§ 211.100(b) and 211.160(a)
Original	§§ 211.180 and 211.194(a)
Accurate	§§ 211.22(a), 211.68, 211.188, and 212.60(g)

4.2.2 FDASIA

The Food and Drug Administration Safety and Innovation Act (FDASIA),[8] signed into law on July 9, 2012, expands the FDA's authorities and strengthens the agency's ability to safeguard and advance public health by:

- Giving the authority to collect user fees from industry to fund reviews of innovator drugs, medical devices, generic drugs, and biosimilar biological products

- Promoting innovation to speed patient access to safe and effective products

- Increasing stakeholder involvement in FDA processes

- Enhancing the safety of the drug supply chain

With nearly 40% of finished drugs being imported, and nearly 80% of active ingredients coming from overseas sources, protecting the global drug supply chain and making sure patients have access to the drugs they need is a priority for the FDA. The FDASIA includes a set of provisions, contained in Title VII of the statute, which give the FDA new authorities to address the challenges posed by an increasingly global drug supply chain. Among them, it requires an establishment that is engaged in the manufacture or preparation

---

[8]   https://www.fda.gov/RegulatoryInformation/LawsEnforcedbyFDA/SignificantAmendmentstotheFDCAct/FDASIA/default.htm. Accessed December 29, 2018.

of a drug to provide the FDA with records or other information in advance of an inspection. Specifically, two of its 18 sections are related to records and data:

Sec. 706—Records for Inspection. This section allows the FDA to obtain certain records and other information from a drug manufacturer in lieu of or in advance of an inspection. The request for information must include a description of the information requested, and the information shall be provided within a reasonable time frame, within reasonable limits, and in a reasonable manner. In one program, the FDA's Office of Regulatory Affairs (ORA) has requested and reviewed records in advance of a number of already-planned inspections conducted by the ORA, and is using the results to inform its agency-wide policy and process to ensure similar requests are carefully implemented. The updated agency-wide procedures describe use of this authority.

In a second program, the FDA's Office of Pharmaceutical Quality is leading the development of policy on applying this section to its Quality Metrics program in order to: (1) inform the risk-based inspection frequency model in advance of inspections (refer to Sec. 510(h) of the Food, Drug, and Cosmetic Act [FD&C Act]), and (2) identify signals for early detection of potential public health incidents (for example, interruption in drug supply).

Sec. 707—Prohibition against Delaying, Denying, Limiting, or Refusing Inspection. This section deems adulterated any drug that is manufactured in an establishment that delays, limits, denies, or refuses to permit entry or inspection. On July 12, 2013, the FDA issued a draft guidance, and on October 22, 2014, the FDA issued final guidance with examples of the types of conduct the FDA considers to be in violation of Section 501(j) of the FD&C Act. This guidance ("Guidance for Industry: Circumstances that Constitute Delaying, Denying, Limiting, or Refusing a Drug Inspection")[9] also specified that, under certain circumstances, delaying, denying, limiting, or refusing a request for records in advance or in lieu of an inspection under Section 706 may also result in a manufacturer's drugs being adulterated under the FD&C Act.

4.2.3 Preapproval inspections

Denoting the importance of data integrity controls, the U.S. FDA allocated to the review of data integrity one of the three goals the agency established during the drug's preapproval inspection process.[10] These three goals are:

---

[9] https://www.fda.gov/downloads/RegulatoryInformation/Guidances/UCM360484 .PDF. Accessed December 29, 2018.

[10] FDA's Compliance Program Guidance Manuel, Program 7346.832, "Preapproval Inspections," https://www.fda.gov/downloads/drugs/developmentapprovalprocess /manufacturing/questionsandanswersoncurrentgoodmanufacturingpracticescgmpfor drugs/ucm071871.PDF. Accessed December, 29, 2018.

- Whether the site has a quality system that is designed to achieve sufficient control over the facility and commercial manufacturing operations

- That the formulation, manufacturing, or processing methods, and analytical (or examination) methods, are consistent with descriptions contained in the application for the biobatch (and other pivotal clinical batches, when applicable), the proposed commercial scale batch, and the active pharmaceutical ingredients (APIs)

- Integrity of raw data and all relevant data

Specifically, the objective 3 "Data Integrity Audit" establishes the following:

Audit the raw data, hard copy or electronic, to authenticate the data submitted in the chemistry, manufacturing, and controls (CMC) section of the application. Verify that all relevant data (e.g., stability, biobatch data) were submitted in the CMC section such that Center for Drug Evaluation and Research (CDER) product reviewers can rely on the submitted data as complete and accurate.

Audit the accuracy and completeness of data in the CMC section for the quality and specifications of components and finished product, and if submitted, data in the development report. Not every CMC data summary must be audited to accomplish this objective. The inspection strategy may select key data sets or randomly select data filed in the application. Generally, data on finished product stability, dissolution, content uniformity, and API impurity are good candidates for this audit.

The review must include data summary tables. Typically, applicants also submit additional testing for the finished product's performance and physicochemical attributes. During the inspection, compare raw data, hard copy or electronic, such as chromatograms, spectrograms, laboratory analyst notebooks, and additional information from the laboratory with summary data filed in the CMC section. Raw data files must support a conclusion that the data/information in the application is complete and enables an objective analysis by reflecting the full range of data/information about the component or finished product known to the establishment. Examples of a lack of contextual integrity include the failure by the applicant to scientifically justify nonsubmission of relevant data, such as aberrant test results or absences in a submitted chromatographic sequence, suggesting the application does not fully or accurately represent the components, process, and finished product.

When data integrity discrepancies are observed, the inspection must identify firm personnel responsible for application submissions and any decision to include or exclude data from the application. Determine what actions or inactions contributed to the data integrity problem and whether any corrective actions were or are to be taken. The inspection must determine if data were not submitted to the application that must have been. For example:

- Was there any "passing" (within specification or otherwise favorable) data submitted to the application that was substituted in place of "failing" data (out of specification, or unfavorable) without a sufficient investigation and resolution of the discrepancy?

- Did the firm improperly invalidate out of specification results, which were therefore not submitted in the application?

The following are possible indications of data integrity problems:

- Alteration of raw, original data and records (for example, the use of correction fluid)

- References to failing biostudies

- Discrepancies (for example, color, shape, embossing) between biostudy samples and reserve samples

- Inconsistencies in manufacturing documentation (for example, identification of actual equipment used) and other information in the submission

The following are some examples of data integrity problems that have been previously observed:

- Multiple analyses of assay done with the same sample without adequate justification

- Exclusion of specific lots from the stability program to avoid submitting failed results

- Reworking or process modifications not adequately justified nor appropriately reported

- Manipulation of a poorly defined analytical procedure and associated data analysis in order to obtain passing results

- Backdating stability test results to meet the required commitments

- Creating acceptable test results without performing the test

- Using test results from previous batches to substitute testing for another batch

- Determination that a site does not actually manufacture the drug as described in the drug application or the Drug Master Files (DMFs) referenced therein; inspection team must determine if the operations appear beyond the capability of the firm and review various production records to determine if batches were truly produced at the site, or are being produced at a subcontracted "shadow factory" without FDA knowledge

This section of the PAI guidelines finishes by including the regulatory foundations of this data integrity goal:

- For finished pharmaceuticals, 21 CFR 314.50(d) requires that the CMC section include "data and information in sufficient detail to permit the agency to make a knowledgeable judgment about whether to approve the application." Several cGMP regulations require laboratory data to be collected and maintained, including § 211.160 (General Requirements), § 211.165 (Testing and Release for Distribution), § 211.166 (Stability), and § 211.167 (Special Testing Requirements).

- For APIs, several sections of the ICH Q7 guidance require laboratory data to be collected and maintained, including Sections 11.1 (Laboratory Controls-General Controls) through 11.5 (Stability Monitoring of APIs).

The FDA is not unique in establishing and updating requirements and guidance regarding good data management principles to ensure data integrity. Following are details about requirements from EMA, PIC/S, MHRA, WHO, and the International Standardization Organization (ISO).

The scope of the MHRA and WHO guidance documents includes the entirety of GXP. The PIC/S guidance on the same topic addresses GMP and GDP, and the EMA and FDA guidance documents address GMP, although the principles are relevant to GXP.

4.3 EU EMA

Among the key efforts made by EMA regarding data integrity, the Annex 11 "Computerized Systems" of the EudraLex Volume 4 GMP for Medicinal Products for Human and Veterinary Use was revised and expanded in 2011 to provide additional clarification for computer system requirements.

In August 2016, the EMA released a new guidance, establishing that data integrity is key to public health protection. The objective of the guidance is to ensure the integrity of data that are generated in the process of testing, manufacturing, packaging, distributing, and monitoring of medicines. Regulators rely on these data to evaluate the quality, safety, and efficacy of medicines and to monitor their benefit-risk profile throughout their life span. Controlling data records helps ensure the data generated are accurate and consistent to support good decision making by both pharmaceutical manufacturers and regulatory authorities.

The EMA's guidance was developed as a set of questions and answers with advice for stakeholders on measures that ensure data integrity and minimize risks at all stages of the data life cycle in pharmaceutical quality systems. The advice applies to both paper-based and electronic systems. It specifically addresses:

- Assessment of risks to data integrity in the collection, processing, and storage of data

- Risk management measures at various stages of the data life cycle

- Design and control of both electronic and paper-based documentation systems

- Measures to ensure data integrity for activities contracted out to another company

The questions and answers describe foundational principles for data integrity and are aligned with previous GMP guidance published by PIC/S described in Section 4.5.

Data integrity enables good decision making by pharmaceutical manufacturers and regulatory authorities. It is a fundamental requirement of the pharmaceutical quality system described in EU GMP Chapter 1, applying equally to manual (paper) and electronic systems.

Promotion of a quality culture, together with implementation of organizational and technical measures that ensure data integrity, is the responsibility of senior management. It requires participation and commitment by staff at all levels within the company, by the company's suppliers, and by its distributors.

Senior management must ensure data integrity risk is assessed, mitigated, and communicated in accordance with the principles of quality risk management. The effort and resource assigned to data integrity measures must be commensurate with the risk to product quality and balanced with other quality assurance resource demands. Where long-term measures are identified in order to achieve the desired state of control, interim measures must be implemented to mitigate risk and must be monitored for effectiveness.

The importance of data integrity to quality assurance and public health protection must be included and discussed in personnel training programs.

The main regulatory expectation for data integrity is to comply with the requirement of ALCOA principles. Table 4.2 provides for each ALCOA principle the link to EU GMP references related to dosage forms (Part I), active substances (Part II), and computerized systems (Annex 11) published in EudraLex Volume 4.[11]

These correspondences have been verified at the time of this writing (December 29, 2018) and refer to the following EudraLex chapters:

- Part I, Chapter 4, "Documentation," effective June 30, 2011

- Part I, Chapter 6, "Quality Control," effective October 1, 2014

- Part II, Chapter 5, "Process Equipment (Computerized System)," effective September 1, 2014

- Part II, Chapter 6, "Documentation and Records," effective September 1, 2014

- Annex 11, "Computerized System," effective June 30, 2011

Comparison of FDA and EMA guidance documents. The EMA guidance contains 23 questions related to data integrity, and the FDA draft guidance addresses 18 questions. Both provide detailed information about the predicate rules and chapters/annexes that are applicable in specific situations. Both emphasize that data integrity enforcement does not represent new requirements or a change in requirements, but rather a reinforcing and clarification of existing requirements as applied to both paper and electronic GMP records.

The two guidance documents have significant similarities, including the following:

- Both include controls over electronic records and paper records

- Both discuss access controls that must be applied to computer systems

- Paper printouts of some data, particularly data that were originally generated electronically (dynamic records as defined by the FDA), do not represent complete data

- Training of staff must include data integrity principles

- Both emphasize the importance of audit trails and their periodic review

---

[11] https://ec.europa.eu/health/documents/eudralex/vol-4_en. Accessed December 29, 2018.

Table 4.2 ALCOA principles and requirements in EU EudraLex Volume 4

ALCOA principle	Part I: Basic requirements for medicinal products	Part II: Basic requirements for active substances	Annex 11: Computerized system
Attributable	• 4.20 c and f • 4.2 c and i • 4.29 point 5	• 5.43 • 6.14 • 6.18 • 6.52	• 2 • 12.1 • 12.4 • 15
Legible	• 4.1 • 4.2 • 4.7 • 4.8 • 4.9 • 4.10	• 6.11 • 6.14 • 6.15 • 6.50	• 4.8 • 7.1 • 7.2 • 8.1 • 9 • 10 • 17
Contemporaneous	• 4.8	• 6.14	• 12.4 • 14
Original	• 4.9 • 4.27 • Paragraph "Record"	• 6.14 • 6.15 • 6.16	• 8.2 • 9
Accurate	• 4.1 • 6.17	• 5.40 • 5.42 • 5.45 • 5.46 • 5.47 • 6.6	• Paragraph "Principles" • 4.8 • 5 • 6 • 7.2 • 10 • 11

- Both address control over blank forms and templates

There are several differences between the two guidance documents, mainly in terminology and focus. Among them:

- The EMA guidance uses an ICH-focused approach, with multiple mentions of the concepts of "life cycle" and "risk" assessments

- The EMA guidance addresses responsibilities for contracted services and their oversight regarding data management and integrity, while the FDA does not address the concept

4.4 UK MHRA

The UK's MHRA took the lead within the EMA countries to identify and detail requirements for data integrity beyond the requirements of Annex 11. At the end of 2013, MHRA announced that the pharmaceutical industry must review data integrity during internal audits. Its "GMP Data Integrity Definitions and Guidance for Industry" document was first issued in January 2015 before being updated in March 2015. In March 2018, MHRA published the "GXP Data Integrity Guidance and Definitions" document, expanding the GMP scope of the 2015 version to the entirety of GXP, similarly to the WHO guidance described in Section 4.6 of this book.[12] The 2018 GXP data integrity guidance document superseded the GMP data integrity guide of March 2015.

The GXP data integrity guidance has a high degree of alignment with documents published by other regulators such as PIC/S, WHO, or the Organisation for Economic Co-operation and Development (OECD) guidance and advisory documents on GLP, and EMA. It is designed to facilitate compliance through education, whilst clarifying the MHRA's position on data integrity and the minimum expectation to achieve compliance.

This document provides guidance on the data integrity expectations that must be considered by organizations involved in any aspect of the pharmaceutical life cycle or GLP studies regulated by MHRA.

The guidance is intended to be a useful resource on the core elements of a compliant data governance system across all GXP sectors (good laboratory practice, good clinical practice, good manufacturing practice, good distribution practice, and good pharmacovigilance practice). It addresses

---

[12] https://assets.publishing.service.gov.uk/government/uploads/system/uploads /attachment_data/file/687246/MHRA_GxP_data_integrity_guide_March_edited _Final.PDF. Accessed December 28, 2018.

fundamental failures identified by MHRA and international regulatory partners during GLP, GCP, GMP, and GDP inspections, many of which have resulted in regulatory action.

4.5 PIC/S

Data integrity guidance documents from PIC/S and WHO (see next section) provide more granularity and examples than do the FDA, EMA, or MHRA guidance documents. The content and requirements are similar, though the organization is different. Both PIC/S and WHO reflect the ALCOA+ attributes for data, requiring that they be attributable, legible, contemporaneous, original, accurate, complete, consistent, enduring, and available.

The PIC/S guidance (draft 3), titled "Good Practices for Data Management and Integrity in Regulated GMP/GDP Environments," was published November 30, 2018.[13] Although it is intended to be used by inspectors in "interpretation of GMP/GDP requirements in relation to data integrity and the conduct of inspections" as the guidance establishes, it constitutes an excellent source of information about this topic.

Consistent with the FDA and EMA, PIC/S states that the guidance does not impose additional requirements, but rather provides guidance on the interpretation of existing PIC/S requirements. Thus, predicate rules and existing requirements provide the framework for ensuring integrity of data. It is written for GMP/GDP, but the principles are applicable to GXP systems.

PIC/S participating authorities regularly undertake inspections of manufacturers and distributors of API and medicinal products in order to determine the level of compliance with GMP/GDP principles. These inspections are commonly performed onsite, however, and may be performed through the remote or offsite evaluation of documentary evidence, in which case the limitations of remote review of data must be considered. The effectiveness of these inspection processes is determined by the veracity of the evidence provided to the inspector and ultimately the integrity of the underlying data. It is critical to the inspection process that inspectors can determine and fully rely on the accuracy and completeness of evidence and records presented to them.

The integrity of data is fundamental to good manufacturing practice and the requirements for good data management are embedded in the current PIC/S guides to GMP/GDP for medicinal products.

Table 4.3 provides for each ALCOA principle the link to PIC/S GMP references related to dosage forms (Part I), active substances (Part II), com-

---

[13] https://www.picscheme.org/layout/document.php?id=1566. Accessed December 14, 2018.

Table 4.3   ALCOA+ principles and requirements in PIC/S guides

ALCOA principle	Part I: PIC/S guide to GMP for medicinal products, PE009	Part II: PIC/S guide to GMP for medicinal products, PE009	Annex 11: Computerized system	PIC/S guide to good distribution practices for medicinal products, PE011
Attributable	• 4.20 c and f • 4.2 c and i • 4.29 point 5	• 5.43 • 6.14 • 6.18 • 6.52	• 2 • 12.1 • 12.4 • 15	• 4.2.4 • 4.2.5
Legible	• 4.1 • 4.2 • 4.7 • 4.8 • 4.9 • 4.10	• 6.11 • 6.14 • 6.15 • 6.50	• 4.8 • 7.1 • 7.2 • 8.1 • 9 • 10 • 17	• 4.2.3 • 4.2.9
Contemporaneous	• 4.8	• 6.14	• 12.4 • 14	• 4.1 • 4.2.9
Original	• 4.9 • 4.27 • Paragraph "Record"	• 6.14 • 6.15 • 6.16	• 8.2 • 9	• 4.2.5
Accurate	• 4.1 • 6.17	• 5.40 • 5.42 • 5.45 • 5.46 • 5.47 • 6.6	• Paragraph "Principles" • 4.8 • 5 • 6 • 7.2 • 10 • 11	• 4.2.3

Table 4.3 ALCOA+ principles and requirements in PIC/S guides (continued)

ALCOA principle	Part I: PIC/S guide to GMP for medicinal products, PE009	Part II: PIC/S guide to GMP for medicinal products, PE009	Annex 11: Computerized system	PIC/S guide to good distribution practices for medicinal products, PE011
Complete	• 4.8	• 6.16 • 6.50 • 6.60 • 6.61	• 4.8 • 7.1 • 7.2 • 9	• 4.23 • 4.25
Consistent	• 4.2	• 6.15 • 6.50	• 4.8 • 5	• 4.23
Enduring	• 4.1 • 4.10	• 6.11 • 6.12 • 6.14	• 7.1 • 17	• 4.2.6
Available	• Paragraph "Principles" • 4.1	• 6.12 • 6.15 • 6.16	• 3.4 • 7.1 • 16 • 17	• 4.2.1

puterized systems (Annex 11), and good distribution practices published in PIC/S guides.

The PIC/S guide to good distribution practices for medicinal product (PE011) was published June 1, 2014, as a guidance document.[14] This guide is based on the EU "Guidelines on Good Distribution Practice (GDP) of Medicinal Products for Human Use." Its Chapter 4 includes the documentation requirements described below, which are closely related to good data management and data integrity principles.

---

[14] https://www.picscheme.org/layout/document.php?id=149. Accessed December 28, 2018.

4.1 PRINCIPLE—Good documentation constitutes an essential part of the quality system. Written documentation must prevent errors from spoken communication and permits the tracking of relevant operations during the distribution of medicinal products. Records must be made at the time each operation is undertaken.

4.2 GENERAL

4.2.1 Documentation comprises all written procedures, instructions, contracts, records, and data, in paper or in electronic form. Documentation must be readily available/retrievable.

4.2.2 With regard to the processing of personal data of employees, complainants, or any other natural person, national legislation on the protection of individuals applies to the processing of personal data and to the free movement of such data.

4.2.3 Documentation must be sufficiently comprehensive with respect to the scope of the wholesale distributor's activities and in a language understood by personnel. It must be written in clear, unambiguous language and be free from errors.

4.2.4 Documentation must be approved, signed, and dated by designated persons, as required. It must not be handwritten, although, where it is necessary, sufficient space must be provided for such entries.

4.2.5 Any alteration made in the documentation must be signed and dated; the alteration must permit the reading of the original information. Where appropriate, the reason for the alteration must be recorded.

4.2.6 Documents must be retained for the period stated in national legislation but at least five years. Personal data must be deleted or anonymized as soon as their storage is no longer necessary for the purpose of distribution activities.

4.2.7 Each employee must have ready access to all necessary documentation for the tasks executed.

4.2.8 Attention must be paid to using valid and approved procedures. Documents must have unambiguous content; title, nature, and purpose must be clearly stated. Documents must be reviewed regularly and kept up to date. Version control must be applied to procedures. After revision of a document, a system must exist to prevent inadvertent use of the superseded version. Superseded or obsolete procedures must be removed from workstations and archived.

4.2.9 Records must be kept either in the form of purchase/sales invoices, delivery slips, or on computer or any other form, for any transaction in medicinal products received or supplied. Records must include at least the following information: date; name of the medicinal product; quantity received, supplied; name and address of the supplier, customer, or consignee, as appropriate; and batch number, expiry date, as required by national legislation. Records are made contemporaneously and, if handwritten, in clear, legible, and indelible handwriting.

4.6 WHO

The WHO "Guidance on Good Data and Record Management Practices, WHO Technical Series No. 996, 2016, Annex 5," published in May 2016, applies to GXP systems.[15] This document was originally published in September 2015 as a draft for comment purposes. The approved document includes a single appendix titled "Expectations and Examples of Special Risk Management Considerations for the Implementation of ALCOA+ Principles in Paper-Based and Electronic Systems."

4.7 ISO 13485:2016

The third edition of the ISO 13485 "Medical Devices—Quality Management Systems—Requirements for Regulatory Purposes" was published March 1, 2016. It established under Section 4.2.5 "Control of Records" the following requirements:

- Records shall be maintained to provide evidence of conformity to requirements and of the effective operation of the quality management system

- The organization shall document procedures to define the controls needed for the identification, storage, security and integrity, retrieval, retention time, and disposition of records

---

[15] http://apps.who.int/medicinedocs/documents/s22402en/s22402en.PDF. Accessed December 26, 2018.

- The organization shall define and implement methods for protecting confidential health information contained in records in accordance with the applicable regulatory requirements

- Records shall remain legible, readily identifiable, and retrievable. Changes to a record shall remain identifiable.

- The organization shall retain the records for at least the lifetime of the medical device as defined by the organization, or as specified by applicable regulatory requirements, but not less than two years from the medical device release by the organization

5

Regulatory Enforcement

5.1 CONSEQUENCES OF LACK OF DATA INTEGRITY: REGULATORY IMPACT

Nowadays, failures in data integrity and data governance represent nearly 80% of FDA warning letters issued to both domestic and foreign pharmaceutical manufacturing sites. Deficiencies included in recent warning letters are remarkably similar to bad practices uncovered over the past 20 years.

Some data integrity breaches detected by FDA inspections are shocking. They range from backdating records in the presence of two FDA inspectors[1] and documenting microbial results on a certificate of analysis when the testing was never performed[2] to removing laboratory instruments from the facility for the duration of the inspection to conceal data manipulations.[3] Some of those egregious examples are discussed in Section 5.4.

Consequences of earlier data integrity scandals during the 1980s were discussed in Section 4.2, and they included the implementation of the Application Integrity Policy and the approval of the Generic Drug Enforcement Act of 1992, which included provisions for debarment of corporations and individuals and the suspension of product distribution among others.

Typical consequences for a firm caught by the FDA with data integrity/data governance problems ranged from a tough inspectional report frequently followed with a warning letter to the halting of preapproval activities for new products and to the inclusion of foreign companies in the import

---

[1] https://www.fda.gov/downloads/Drugs/GuidanceComplianceRegulatoryInformati on/EnforcementActivitiesbyFDA/UCM382514.PDF. Accessed December 27, 2018.

[2] https://www.raps.org/regulatory-focus%E2%84%A2/news-articles/2015/2/india-s -data-integrity-problems. Accessed December 27, 2018.

[3] https://www.fda.gov/ICECI/EnforcementActions/WarningLetters/ucm361553.htm. Accessed December 27, 2018.

alert list. The FDA's immediate expectations once data integrity issues are discovered are discussed in Sections 12.2 and 12.3.

Import alert. Foreign firms in which the FDA discovers significant problem related to data integrity and data governance typically receive a warning letter and most of the time are included in the red list of import alerts. Import alerts inform FDA field staff and the public that the agency has enough evidence to allow for Detention without Physical Examination (DWPE) of products that appear to be in violation of FDA laws and regulations. The FDA has jurisdiction over imported products at the time of entry but also after the products have entered domestic commerce. Although there are dozens of different types of import alerts, data integrity and data governance issues are classified under the general category knows as Import Alert #66-40, defined as "Detention without Physical Examination of Drugs from Firms which Have Not Met Drug GMPs."[4]

Reasons for alerts are described as follows: "Foreign inspections of pharmaceutical manufacturers are being performed. Detention without physical examination may be appropriate when an FDA inspection has revealed that a firm is not operating in conformity with current good manufacturing practices (GMPs). The article is subject to refusal of admission pursuant to Section 801(a)(3) in that the methods and controls used in its manufacture and control of pharmaceutical products do not appear to conform to current good manufacturing practices within the meaning of Section 501(a)(2)(B)."

The FDA might also include a foreign firm in the Import Alert #66-40 when the FDA receives information concerning inspections conducted by foreign or other government authorities under a Memorandum of Understanding or other agreement that the FDA concludes reveals conditions or practices warranting detention of either particular products or all products manufactured by a firm. DWPE of such firms remains in effect until such time as the FDA is satisfied that the appearance of a violation has been removed, either by reinspection or submission of appropriate documentation to the responsible FDA Center.

Data integrity and data governance remain a principal focus of global regulatory authorities not just the U.S. FDA. As previously mentioned, good data integrity and data governance practices are also requirements for good clinical practices. Several major cases were discovered at sites performing bioequivalence and bioavailabity studies to support generic product approval. These situations typically impact hundreds of products and upon discovering of these cases, sponsors must frequently repeat the studies at different clinical sites.

---

4   https://www.accessdata.fda.gov/cms_ia/importalert_189.html. Accessed December 27, 2018.

Two recent examples are GVK Biosciences (Hyderabad, India) and Semler Research Private Limited (Bangalore, India).

In the case of **GVK Biosciences**, more than 700 generic products were recommended for suspension by EMA over flawed studies. On May 21, 2015, the EMA confirmed its recommendation to suspend a number of medicines for which authorization in the EU was primarily based on clinical studies conducted at GVK Biosciences. This is the outcome of a reexamination requested by marketing authorization holders for seven of the products concerned.

EMA's Committee for Medicinal Products for Human Use (CHMP) adopted its original recommendation of January 2015 following an inspection of GVK Biosciences's site at Hyderabad by the French agency ANSM that raised concerns about how GVK Biosciences conducted studies at the site on behalf of marketing authorization holders.

The inspection revealed data manipulations of ECGs while carrying out studies of generic medicines, which appeared to have taken place over a period of at least five years. Their systematic nature, including the extended period of time during which they took place and the number of members of staff involved, cast doubt on the integrity of the conduct of trials at the site generally and on the reliability of data generated.

During the reexamination, the CHMP concluded that concerns about the reliability of the clinical studies remain and therefore maintained its recommendation of January 2015 to suspend medicines for which no supporting data from other studies were available. This is with the exception of one medicine included in the reexamination for which concerns about studies were addressed. This medicine was removed from the list of medicines recommended for suspension.

As a result of the CHMP's January 2015 opinion and the reexamination, around 700 pharmaceutical forms and strengths of medicines studied at the Hyderabad site were recommended for suspension. For around 300 other pharmaceutical forms and strengths, sufficient supporting data from other sources had been provided; these medicines therefore remained on the market in the EU.

Regarding **Semler Research**, the following notice was posted on the FDA website one day after the agency sent a letter to Semler Research Center, which is based in Bangalore, India, saying that inspection found significant instances of misconduct and violations of federal regulations, including the substitution and manipulation of study subject samples.[5] The title of the notice is also significant: "Notification to Pharmaceutical Companies: Clinical and Bioanalytical Studies Conducted by Semler Research Are Unacceptable."

---

[5] https://www.fda.gov/Drugs/DrugSafety/ucm495778.htm. Accessed December 27, 2018.

[4/20/2016] FDA is notifying sponsors of New Drug Applications (NDAs) and Abbreviated New Drug Applications (ANDAs) that clinical and bioanalytical studies conducted by Semler Research Private Limited (Semler) located in Bangalore, India, are not acceptable as a result of data integrity concerns, and need to be repeated. Semler is a contract research organization that conducts bioequivalence and bioavailability studies for a number of pharmaceutical companies.

FDA is taking this action as a result of an inspection of Semler's bioanalytical facility in Bangalore, India, conducted between September 29, 2015, and October 9, 2015. The inspection found significant instances of misconduct and violations of federal regulations, including the substitution and manipulation of study subject samples. Yesterday, FDA issued an "Untitled Letter" to Semler detailing our findings related to the facility. A copy of this letter is available below.

FDA has evaluated drugs that were approved based on data from Semler that supported approval during the regulatory review process. FDA has conducted a thorough review of postmarket serious adverse events for all drug products which had studies conducted at Semler facilities. To date, the agency has not identified reports that raise serious safety concerns with these products. However, FDA is requiring that sponsors of approved applications repeat the bioequivalence/bioavailability studies using an entity other than Semler. FDA is also changing the therapeutic equivalence (TE) rating in FDA's Approved Drug Product with Therapeutic Equivalence Evaluations (the Orange Book) for any approved ANDA that relied on data from Semler to "BX." A BX rating indicates that data reviewed by the agency are insufficient to determine therapeutic equivalence, i.e., substitutability, of the generic product to the drug it references.

FDA is sending letters to sponsors of applications that are currently under review that include data from studies conducted at Semler. The letter informs the sponsor that it must repeat the bioequivalence/bioavailability studies using an entity other than Semler at an acceptable alternate study site.

Affected sponsors are encouraged to review the documents below and contact the relevant FDA review division in the Office of Generic Drugs or the Office of New Drugs for further information.

Previously, the WHO issued a "Notice of Concern"[6] to Semler for the same reasons. Specifically, the WHO examined company computer servers

---

6   https://extranet.who.int/prequal/sites/default/files/documents/NOC_Semler12April 2016.PDF. Accessed December 27, 2018.

and found a spreadsheet file containing detailed instructions for manipulating drug samples that were used in clinical trials for its clients. "Manipulation of at least five studies over an extended period of time indicates this is a common practice," the WHO wrote. "WHO is of the impression that to execute this type of manipulation, several staff members on various levels within the organization have to be collaborating and coordinating. The issue is thus not confined to a single person operating outside of the quality management system."

The WHO noted that Semler acknowledged there were four FDA studies, and one WHO study that had questionable data that could not be explained. Consequences at Semler included the FDA's Form 483, a FDA untitled letter, a WHO notice of concern, and an EMA recommendation of suspension.

Probably the pharmaceutical company that epitomizes the lack of good data governance and data integrity is **Ranbaxy Laboratory Limited**, an Indian company incorporated in 1961. The company went public in 1973, and Japanese pharmaceutical company Daiichi Sankyo acquired a controlling share in 2008. In 2014, Sun Pharma acquired the entire share of Ranbaxy, making the conglomerate the world's fifth-largest specialty generic pharma company. Ranbaxy was one of the few companies included in the FDA's Application Integrity Policy List.

FDA regulatory actions against Ranbaxy include numerous warning letters (since 2006), import alerts (since 2008), and several consent decrees in 2012 through 2013. In May 2013, the company pleaded guilty to several felony charges and agreed to pay $500 million to resolve false claims allegations, cGMP violations, and false statements to the FDA. Following is the U.S. Department of Justice official communication regarding this settlement:[7]

> In the largest drug safety settlement to date with a generic drug manufacturer, Ranbaxy USA, a subsidiary of Indian generic pharmaceutical manufacturer Ranbaxy Laboratories Limited, pleaded guilty today to felony charges relating to the manufacture and distribution of certain adulterated drugs made at two of Ranbaxy's manufacturing facilities in India, the Justice Department announced today. Ranbaxy also agreed to pay a criminal fine and forfeiture totaling $150 million and to settle civil claims under the False Claims Act and related State laws for $350 million.
>
> The federal Food, Drug, and Cosmetic Act (FDCA) prohibits the introduction or delivery for introduction into interstate commerce of any drug that is adulterated. Under the FDCA, a drug

---

[7] https://www.justice.gov/opa/pr/generic-drug-manufacturer-ranbaxy-pleads-guilty
-and-agrees-pay-500-million-resolve-false. Accessed December 27, 2018.

is adulterated if the methods used in, or the facilities or controls used for, its manufacturing, processing, packing, or holding do not conform to, or are not operated or administered in conformity with, current Good Manufacturing Practice (cGMP) regulations. This assures that a drug meets the requirements as to safety and has the identity and strength, and meets the quality and purity characteristics, which the drug purports or is represented to possess.

Ranbaxy USA pleaded guilty to three felony FDCA counts, and four felony counts of knowingly making material false statements to the FDA. The generic drugs at issue were manufactured at Ranbaxy's facilities in Paonta Sahib and Dewas, India. Under the plea agreement, the company will pay a criminal fine of $130 million, and forfeit an additional $20 million.

"When companies sell adulterated drugs, they undermine the integrity of the FDA's approval process and may cause patients to take drugs that are substandard, ineffective, or unsafe," said Stuart F. Delery, Acting Assistant Attorney General for the Civil Division of the Department of Justice. "We will continue to work with our law enforcement partners to ensure that all manufacturers of drugs approved by the FDA for sale in the United States, both domestic and foreign, follow the FDA guidelines that protect all of us."

"This is the largest false claims case ever prosecuted in the District of Maryland, and the nation's largest financial penalty paid by a generic pharmaceutical company for FDCA violations," said U.S. Attorney for the District of Maryland Rod J. Rosenstein. "The joint criminal and civil settlement, which reflects many years of work by FDA agents and federal prosecutors, holds Ranbaxy accountable for a pattern of violations and must improve the reliability of generic drugs manufactured in India by Ranbaxy."

Ranbaxy USA admitted to introducing into interstate commerce certain batches of adulterated drugs that were produced at Paonta Sahib in 2005 and 2006, including Sotret, gabapentin, and ciprofloxacin. Sotret is Ranbaxy's branded generic form of isotretinoin, a drug used to treat severe recalcitrant nodular acne; gabapentin is a drug used to treat epilepsy and nerve pain; ciprofloxacin is a broad-spectrum antibiotic. In a Statement of Facts filed along with the Information, Ranbaxy USA acknowledged that FDA's inspection of the Paonta Sahib facility in 2006 found incomplete testing records and an inadequate program to assess the stability characteristics of drugs. "Stability" refers to how the quality of a drug varies with time under the influence of a variety of factors, such as temperature, humidity, and light. Such testing is used to determine appropriate storage conditions and expiration dates for the drug, as well as to detect any impurities in the drug.

Ranbaxy also acknowledged that the FDA's 2006 and 2008 inspections of the Dewas facility found the same issues with incomplete testing records and an inadequate stability program, as well as significant cGMP deviations in the manufacture of certain active pharmaceutical ingredients and finished products. Ranbaxy USA also acknowledged that in 2003 and 2005 the company was informed of cGMP violations by consultants it hired to conduct audits at the Paonta Sahib and Dewas facilities. Those cGMP violations resulted in the introduction into interstate commerce of some adulterated drugs.

Ranbaxy USA further admitted to failing to timely file required reports known to FDA as "field alerts" for batches of Sotret and gabapentin that had failed certain tests. With respect to Sotret, Ranbaxy USA was aware in January 2003 that a batch of Sotret failed an accelerated dissolution stability test but continued to distribute the batch into the United States for another 13 months. With respect to gabapentin, Ranbaxy USA was aware at various times between June and August 2007 that certain batches of gabapentin were testing out-of-specification, had unknown impurities, and would not maintain their expected shelf life. Nevertheless, Ranbaxy USA did not notify FDA and institute a voluntary recall until October 2007.

Ranbaxy USA also admitted to making false, fictitious, and fraudulent statements to the FDA in Annual Reports filed in 2006 and 2007 regarding the dates of stability tests conducted on certain batches of Cefaclor, Cefadroxil, Amoxicillin, and Amoxicillin and Clavulanate Potassium, which were manufactured at the Dewas facility. Ranbaxy USA was found to have conducted stability testing of certain batches of these drugs weeks or months after the dates reported to FDA. In addition, instead of conducting some of the stability tests at prescribed intervals months apart, the tests were conducted on the same day or within a few days of each other. This practice resulted in unreliable test results regarding the shelf life of the drugs. Ranbaxy USA also acknowledged that drug samples waiting to be tested were stored for unknown periods of time in a refrigerator, which did not meet specified temperature and humidity ranges for an approved stability chamber, and that this was not disclosed to the FDA.

As part of the settlement, the whistleblower, Dinesh Thakur, a former Ranbaxy executive, received approximately \$48.6 million from the federal share of the settlement amount.

5.2 FDA DEBARMENT LIST

The Generic Drug Enforcement Act of 1992 includes provision for debarment. Based on that, the FDA can, and sometimes must, impose this penalty on persons or companies that engage in criminal conduct with respect to the development or approval of new drugs. The penalty itself is a prohibition against that person or company from submitting or assisting in the submission of such an application. By statute, it only applies to applications for approval of new drugs, and not to applications for other approvals granted by the FDA, such as changing a prescription drug to over-the-counter status, or approving a new food additive.

As of December 16, 2018, the FDA Debarment List for Drug Product Applications includes 151 debarred persons.[8] Since 2009, the FDA also began to debar food importers. A total of 15 persons are included in this list. Also, a corporate entity was included in the food importer debar list for the first time on March 1, 2018.[9]

In the earliest debarment cases (associated with the "generic scandal"), following the passage of the laws permitting the imposition of this penalty, penalties were imposed retroactively to persons who had committed the offending acts before the passage of those laws.

Scope of debarment. The GDEA prohibits a debarred individual from providing services in any capacity to a person who has an approved or pending drug product application (Section 306(a)(2) and (b)(1) of the act). The agency has interpreted "services in any capacity" to mean any service provided to the drug applicant, regardless of whether it is related to drug regulation. That means a debarred individual may not provide non–drug-related services to a drug product applicant (for example, as a landscaper, a computer software supplier, an accountant, a telephone repair person, a janitor, an interior decorator, a landlord) without violating debarment. Both the firm and individuals are subject to substantial civil penalties for violation of this provision.[10]

---

[8] https://www.fda.gov/iceci/enforcementactions/fdadebarmentlist/default.htm. Accessed December 28, 2018.

[9] https://www.fda.gov/ICECI/EnforcementActions/FDADebarmentList/ucm194263.htm. Accessed December 28, 2018.

[10] https://www.fda.gov/downloads/Drugs/GuidanceComplianceRegulatoryInformation/Guidances/UCM080584.PDF. Accessed December 29, 2018.

5.3 FDA CLINICAL INVESTIGATORS: DISQUALIFICATION PROCEEDINGS

The FDA also regulates scientific studies that are designed to develop evidence to support the safety and effectiveness of investigational drugs (human and animal), biological products, and medical devices. Physicians and other qualified experts ("clinical investigators") who conduct these studies are required to comply with applicable statutes and regulations intended to ensure the integrity of clinical data on which product approvals are based and, for research involving human subjects, to help protect the rights, safety, and welfare of those subjects.

In certain situations, in which the FDA alleges a clinical investigator has violated applicable regulations, the FDA may initiate a clinical investigator disqualification proceeding.[11] The Clinical Investigator: Disqualification Proceedings database provides a list of clinical investigators who are or have been subject to an administrative clinical investigator disqualification action and indicates the current status of that action. As of December 29, 2018, a total of 228 clinical investigators are included in this database.

5.4 FDA ENFORCEMENT

Almost 20 years ago, the FDA began issuing warning letters that identified failures associated with data integrity. Failures or shortcoming in computer system validation, maintenance of electronic records, and the review of laboratory computer systems' audit trail were among the most common citations in those earlier years.

Following these earlier compliance actions, the FDA announced a pilot program in 2010 to include the evaluation of data integrity as part of routine cGMP inspections. It's noteworthy to remark that most of the deficiencies were (and continue to be) failures to comply with predicate regulations (for example, 21 CFR Part § 211) rather than against 21 CFR Part § 11. In fact, deficiencies in Part 11 are rarely cited in enforcement documents.

In the last few years, a string of FDA-issued warning letters for data integrity violations has been published on the agency's website. Another interesting fact is that the percentage of warning letters that cite good documentation practices/data integrity problems issued to U.S. sites in fiscal years 2016 and 2017 is very similar (70% to 80%) when compared to warning

---

[11] https://www.fda.gov/ICECI/EnforcementActions/ucm321308.htm. Accessed December 29, 2018.

letters issued to foreign companies.[12] FDA warning letters are available at the agency web page.[13]

Appendix A depicts several significant enforcement actions related to good documentation practices/data integrity carried out by the FDA and published until end of year 2018.

5.5 NON-U.S. ENFORCEMENT

Regarding non-FDA enforcement actions related to lack of adequate controls for good documentation practices/data integrity, EU regulatory authorities frequently cited violations similar to those cited by FDA inspectors.

In the case of the EU, the EudraGMDP database[14] is maintained and operated by the EMA. Its public section was expanded in 2014 to include reports of noncompliance, many of which address the area of good documentation practices and data integrity identified during inspection conducted by the European authorities.

WHO's notices of concern and notice of suspension can be found at its website.[15]

A notice of concern (NOC) is a letter that is issued to a manufacturer, contract research organization (CRO), or medical quality control laboratory (QCL), by WHO, to remind a manufacturer, CRO, or QCL of its obligation to maintain quality assurance procedures and practices and to inform suppliers and procurement agencies of any potential risks associated with a given product, manufacturer, CRO, or QCL.

A notice of suspension (NOS) is a letter issued by WHO after serious concerns have arisen about the conduct of a manufacturer, or in relation to data and/or information about a prequalified API or finished pharmaceutical product (FPP).

---

[12] https://www.fdli.org/2018/04/update-fda-data-integrity-enforcement-trends-practical-mitigation-measures/. Accessed December 29, 2018.

[13] https://www.fda.gov/ICECI/EnforcementActions/WarningLetters/default.htm. Accessed December 29, 2018.

[14] http://eudragmdp.ema.europa.eu/inspections/gmpc/searchGMPNonCompliance.do. Accessed December 29, 2018.

[15] https://extranet.who.int/prequal/content/notices-concernsuspension. Accessed December 29, 2018.

6

Data Life Cycle

Data life cycle management is a fundamental element of data governance and refers to the:

- Generation and recording of data

- Processing data into usable information

- Checking the completeness and accuracy of reported data and processed information

- Data (or results) that are used to make a decision

- Retaining and retrieval of data that protects it from loss, unauthorized modifications, or amendments

- Retiring or disposal of data in a controlled manner at the end of its life

Data governance must address data ownership and accountability for data process(es) and risk management of the data life cycle. Data life cycle reviews are applicable to both paper and electronic records, although control measures may be applied differently. Segregation of duties between data life cycle stages provides safeguards against data integrity failure by reducing the opportunity for an individual to alter, misrepresent, or falsify data without detection. Data risk must be considered at each stage of the data life cycle review.

Good data process design, based upon process understanding and the application of sound scientific principles, including risk management, will increase the assurance of data integrity and result in effective and efficient business and regulatory processes.

Data integrity can be affected at any stage in its life cycle. It is therefore important to understand the life cycle elements for each type of data or record and ensure controls that are proportionate to data criticality and risk at all stages. Data integrity risks are likely to occur and to be highest when data processes or specific data process steps are inconsistent, subjective, open to bias, unsecured, unnecessarily complex or redundant, duplicated, undefined, not well understood, hybrid, or based upon unproven assumptions, or do not adhere to good documentation practices.

6.1 DATA COLLECTION AND RECORDING

All data collection and recording activities must be performed following good documentation practices and must apply risk-based controls to protect and verify critical/significant data. Regulated companies must have an appropriate level of process understanding and technical knowledge of systems used for data collection and recording, including their capabilities, limitations, and vulnerabilities.

Methods used for data collection and recording must ensure data of appropriate accuracy, completeness, content, and meaning are collected and retained for their intended use. Where the capability of the electronic system permits dynamic storage, it is not appropriate for static (printed/manual) data to be retained in preference to dynamic (electronic) data.

As data are required to allow the full reconstruction of activities, the amount and the level of detail (resolution) of data to be collected must be justified.

When used, blank forms (including, but not limited to, worksheets, laboratory notebooks, and master production and control records) must be controlled. For example, numbered sets of blank forms may be issued and reconciled upon completion. Similarly, bound paginated notebooks, stamped or formally issued by a document control group, allow detection of unofficial notebooks and any gaps in notebook pages.

Potential risks to consider when assessing the generating and recording of data. The following aspects must be considered when determining risk and control measures:

- How and where are original data created (for example, paper or electronic)?

- Does the process require that critical or significant data inputs be verified? Data entries, such as the sample identification for laboratory tests or the recording of source data for inclusion of a patient in a clinical trial, must be verified by a second person or entered through technical means such as barcoding, as appropriate for the intended use of these data. Additional controls may include locking critical data entries after the data are verified and review of audit trails for critical data to detect if they have been altered.

- What metadata is associated with the data to ensure a complete, accurate, and traceable record, following ALCOA principles?

- Does the record permit the reconstruction of the activity?

- Where are the data and metadata located?

- Does the system require that data are saved to permanent memory at the time of recording, or are they held in a temporary memory? In the case of some computerized analytical and manufacturing equipment, data may be stored as a temporary local file prior to transfer to a permanent storage location (server). During the period of "temporary" storage, there is often limited audit trail provision amending, deleting, or recreating data. This is a data integrity risk. Removing the use of temporary memory (or reducing the period that data are stored in temporary memory) reduces the risk of undetected data manipulation.

- Is it possible to recreate, amend, or delete original data and metadata? Computerized system controls may be more complex, including setting of user privileges and system configuration to limit or prevent access to amend data. It is important to review all data access opportunities, including IT helpdesk staff, who may make changes at the request of the data user. These changes must be procedurally controlled, visible, and approved within the quality system.

6.2 DATA TRANSFER AND MIGRATION

Data transfer is the process of transferring data and metadata between different data storage media types, formats, or computerized systems for processing or storage. Data migration is the process of moving stored data from one durable storage location to another. This migration may, if necessary, include changing the format of data (to make it usable or visible on an alternative computerized system), but not the content or meaning.

Data transfer/migration procedures must include the rationale and be robustly designed and validated to ensure data integrity is maintained during the data life cycle. Careful consideration must be given to understanding the data format and the potential for alteration at each stage of data generation, transfer, and subsequent storage. The challenges of migrating data are often underestimated, particularly regarding maintaining the full meaning of the migrated records.

Data transfer must be validated. The data must not be altered during or after they are transferred to the worksheet or other application. There must be an audit trail for this process. Appropriate procedures must be followed if the data transfer during the operation has not occurred correctly. Electronic worksheets used in automation like paper documentation must be version controlled, and any changes in the worksheet must be documented/verified appropriately.

Potential risks to consider when assessing the transfer and migration of data

- Are data protected from possibility of intentional or unintentional loss or modifications/amendment during transfer to other systems?

- Are electronic interfaces validated to demonstrate security and no corruption of data, particularly where systems require an interface to present data in a different structure or file format?

- Does the person processing the data have the ability to influence what data are reported, or how they are presented?

6.3 DATA PROCESSING

Data processing can be defined as the sequence of operations performed on data to extract, present, or obtain information in a defined format. Examples might include the conversion of a raw electronic signal to a chromatogram and subsequently a calculated numerical result, or the statistical analysis of individual patient data to present trends.

There must be adequate traceability of any user-defined parameters used within data processing activities to the raw data, including attribution to who performed the activity.

To ensure data integrity, data processing must be done in an objective manner, free from bias, using validated or verified protocols, processes, methods, systems, and equipment, and according to approved procedures and training programs. Audit trails and retained records must allow reconstruction of all data processing activities regardless of whether the output of that processing is subsequently reported or otherwise used for regulatory or business purposes. If data processing has been repeated with progressive modification of processing parameters, this must be visible to ensure the processing parameters are not being manipulated to achieve a more desirable result.

Potential risks to consider when assessing the processing of data

- How are data processed? Data processing methods must be approved, identifiable, and version controlled. In the case of electronic data processing, methods must be locked where appropriate to prevent unauthorized modification/amendment.

- How is data processing recorded? The processing method must be recorded. In situations where raw data have been processed more than once, each iteration (including method and result) must be available to the data checker for verification.

- Does the person processing the data have the ability to influence what data are reported, or how they are presented? Even validated systems that do not permit the user to make any changes to data may be at risk if the user can choose what data are printed, reported, or transferred for processing. This includes performing the activity multiple times as separate events and reporting a desired outcome from one of these repeats.

  Data presentation (for example, changing scale of graphical reports to enhance or reduce presentation of analytical peaks) can also influence decision making and therefore impact data integrity. Clinical and safety studies must be designed to prevent and detect statistical bias that may occur through improper selection of data to be included in statistical calculations.

6.4 DATA REVIEW, REPORTING, AND APPROVAL

Data must be reviewed and, where appropriate, evaluated statistically after completion of the process to determine whether outcomes are consistent and compliant with established standards. The evaluation must take into consideration *all data*, including atypical, suspect, or rejected data, together with the reported data. This includes a review of the original paper and electronic records.

The approach to reviewing specific record content, such as critical data and metadata, cross-outs on paper records, and audit trails on electronic records, must meet all applicable regulatory requirements and be risk based.

During the data life cycle, data must be subject to continuous monitoring, as appropriate, to enhance process understanding and facilitate knowledge management and informed decision making. To ensure the entire set of data is considered in the reported data, the review of original electronic data must include checks of all locations where data may have been stored, including locations where voided, deleted, invalid, or rejected data may have been stored.

There must be a procedure that describes the process for review and approval of data. Data review must also include a risk-based review of relevant metadata, including relevant audit trail records. Data review must be documented, and the record must include a statement regarding whether issues were found, the date that review was performed, and the signature of the reviewer.

A procedure must describe the actions to be taken if data review identifies an error or omission. This procedure must enable data corrections or clarifications to provide visibility of the original record, and traceability of the correction, using ALCOA principles (see Chapter 2.3.5).

Where data review is not conducted by the organization that generated the data, the responsibilities for data review must be documented and agreed by both parties. Summary reports of data are often supplied between organizations (contract givers and acceptors). It must be acknowledged that summary reports are limited, and critical supporting data and metadata may not be included.

Many software packages allow configuration of customized reports. Key actions may be incorporated into such reports provided they are validated and locked to prevent changes. Automated reporting tools and reports may reduce the checks required to assure the integrity of the data.

Where summary reports are supplied by a different organization (for example, a certificate of analysis), the organization receiving and using the data must evaluate the data provider's data integrity controls and processes prior to using the information.

Potential risks to consider when assessing the completeness and accuracy of reported data and processed information

- Are original data (including the original data format) available for checking? The format of the original data (electronic or paper) must be preserved and available to the data reviewer in a manner that permits interaction with the data (for example, search, query). This approach facilitates a risk-based review of the record and can also reduce administrative burden, for instance, utilizing validated audit trail "exception reports" instead of an onerous line-by-line review.

- Are there any periods when data are not audit trailed? This may present an opportunity for data amendment that is not subsequently visible to the data reviewer. Additional control measures must be implemented to reduce risk of undisclosed data manipulation.

- Does the data reviewer have visibility and access to all data generated? This must include any data from failed or aborted activities, discrepant or unusual data that have been excluded from processing, or the final decision-making process. Visibility of all data provides protection against selective data reporting or "testing into compliance."

- Does the data reviewer have visibility and access to all processing of data? This ensures the final result obtained from raw data (any data exclusion or changes to processing methods) is scientifically sound. Visibility of all processing information provides protection against undisclosed "processing into compliance."

- Are these the only data generated as part of this activity? Are we considering all the data? Whenever out-of-trend or atypical results are obtained, they must be investigated. This includes investigating and determining corrective and preventive actions for invalid runs, failures, repeats, and other atypical data. All data must be included in the data set unless there is a documented scientific explanation for their exclusion.

- When is the pass or fail decision taken? If data acceptability decisions are taken before a record (raw data or processed result) is saved to permanent memory, there may be an opportunity for the user to manipulate data to provide a satisfactory result, without this change being visible in the audit trail. This would not be visible to the data reviewer. This is a particular consideration where computerized systems alert the user to an out-of-specification entry before the data entry process is complete or saves the record in temporary memory.

- Have the data been generated and maintained correctly?

- Are there indicators of unauthorized changes?

- Have there been IT requests to amend any data post review?

- Have there been any system maintenance activities and has the impact of that activity been assessed?

6.5 DATA RETENTION, ARCHIVING, AND RETRIEVAL

Data retention activities include archiving (protected data for long-term storage) and temporary backup (data for the purposes of disaster recovery). Data and document retention arrangements must ensure the protection of records from deliberate or inadvertent alteration or loss. Secure controls must be in place to ensure the data integrity of the record throughout the retention period and must be validated where appropriate (see also Chapter 6.2 on data transfer and migration).

Data (or a true copy) generated in paper format may be retained by using a validated scanning process provided there is a documented process in place to ensure that the outcome is a true copy.

Procedures for destruction of data must consider data criticality and, where applicable, regulatory retention requirements.

A designated secure area or facility (for example, cabinet, room, building, or computerized system) must be used for the long-term retention of data and metadata. Archived records may be the original record or a "true copy" and must be protected so they cannot be altered or deleted without detection and protected against any accidental damage such as fire, humidity, or pest.

Archive arrangements must be designed to permit recovery and readability of the data and metadata throughout the required retention period. In the case of archiving of electronic data, this process must be validated, and in the case of legacy systems, the ability to review data must be periodically verified (for example, to confirm the continued support of legacy computerized systems). Where hybrid records are stored, references between physical and electronic records must be maintained such that full verification of events is possible throughout the retention period.

Only validated systems must be used for storage of data; however, the media used for the storage of data do not have an unlimited lifespan. When legacy systems can no longer be supported, consideration must be given to maintaining the software for data accessibility purposes (for as long possible depending upon the specific retention requirements). This may be achieved by maintaining software in a virtual environment.

Migration to an alternative file format that retains as much as possible of the "true copy" attributes of the data may be necessary with increasing age of the legacy data. Where migration with full original data functionality is not technically possible, options must be assessed based on risk and the importance of the data over time. The migration file format must be selected considering the balance of risk between long-term accessibility versus the possibility of reduced dynamic data functionality (for example, data interrogation, trending, reprocessing, and so on). It is possible that the need to maintain accessibility may require migration to a file format that loses some attributes and/or dynamic data functionality (see also Chapter 6.2 on data transfer and migration).

Data folders on some standalone systems may not include all audit trails or other metadata needed to reconstruct all activities. Other metadata may be found in other electronic folders or in operating system logs. When archiving electronic data, it is important to ensure associated metadata are archived with the relevant data set or securely traceable to the data set through appropriate documentation. The ability to successfully retrieve from the archives the entire data set, including metadata, must be verified.

Potential risks to consider when retaining and retrieving data to protect it from loss or unauthorized modification/amendment

- How and where are data stored? Storage of data (paper or electronic) must be at secure locations, with access limited to authorized persons. The storage location must provide adequate protection from damage due to water, fire, pest, and so on.

- What are the measures protecting against loss or unauthorized modification/amendment? Data security measures must be at least equivalent to those applied during the previous data life cycle stages. Retrospective data amendment (for example via IT helpdesk or database amendments) must be controlled, with appropriate segregation of duties and approval processes.

- Are data backed up in a manner permitting reconstruction of the activity? Backup arrangements must be validated to demonstrate the ability to restore data following IT system failure. In situations where metadata (including relevant operating system event logs) are stored in different file locations from raw data, the backup process must be carefully designed to ensure that all data required to reconstruct a record is included.

  Similarly, true copies of paper records may be duplicated on paper, microfilm, or electronically, and stored in a separate location.

- What are ownership and retrieval arrangements, particularly considering outsourced activities or data storage? A technical/quality agreement must be in place that addresses the specific regulatory requirements for outsourced activities.

- What is the data retention period? This will be influenced by regulatory requirements and data criticality. When considering data for a single product, there may be different data retention needs for different types of data.

- How is data disposal authorized? Any disposal of data must be approved within the quality system and be performed in accordance with a procedure to ensure compliance with the required data retention period.

7

Integrating Data Integrity into the Quality System

7.1 QUALITY SYSTEM OF REGULATED PRODUCTS

A viable quality management system must be based on data and records that are ALCOA. In the case of the medical products, good documentation practices and data integrity are primal concepts to ensure GMP compliance.

Good documentation practices and data integrity are embedded into pharmaceutical national regulations (U.S. FDA, Health Canada, EU's EMA, and so on), as well as into international standards and guidance documents (ICH Q10 Pharmaceutical Quality Systems, WHO's GMP guidelines, PIC/S guidance, and so on). The same scenario is true for medical device regulations, where most of the national regulations follow the International Standard ISO 13485.

Although most of the above-mentioned national and international regulations do not specifically address data integrity issues, between 2015 and 2016, six major international regulatory authorities published guidance documents addressing data management and data integrity. Two of these, the draft guidance published by the U.S. FDA in April 2016 and the guidance posted by the EMA in August 2016, take a question-and-answer approach. The guidance from the UK's MHRA, the CFDA, the PIC/S, and the WHO take a more standard narrative approach to their regulatory guidance. However, all six guidance documents are very similar in their overall expectations.

One of the key responsibilities of senior management must be to ensure there is a data integrity policy for the company, and that it is deployed to all levels within the organization. Integrity of data and good documentation practices is the responsibility of everyone.

The rest of this chapter covers important elements of good documentation practices and data integrity frequently cited by regulators as a source of data integrity mishaps.

7.2 HANDLING OF PAPER RECORDS: LOGBOOKS AND BLANK FORMS

The effective management of paper-based documents is a key element of GMP/GDocP. Accordingly, the documentation system must be designed to meet GMP/GDocP requirements and ensure documents and records are effectively controlled to maintain their integrity. Paper records must be controlled and must remain ALCOA throughout the data life cycle.

When used, blank forms (including, but not limited to, worksheets, laboratory notebooks, and master production and control records) must be controlled. For example, numbered sets of blank forms may be issued and reconciled upon completion. Similarly, bound paginated notebooks, stamped or formally issued by a document control group, allow detection of unofficial notebooks and any gaps in notebook pages.

Procedures outlining good documentation practices and arrangements for document control must be available within the QMS. These procedures must specify:

- How master documents and procedures are created, reviewed, and approved for use

- Generation, distribution, and control of templates used to record data

- Retrieval and disaster recovery processes regarding records

- The process for generation of working copies of documents for routine use, with specific emphasis on ensuring copies of documents (for example, SOPs and blank forms are issued and reconciled for use in a controlled and traceable manner)

- Guidance for the completion of paper-based documents, specifying how individual operators are identified, data entry formats, and how amendments to documents are recorded

- How completed documents are routinely reviewed for accuracy, authenticity, and completeness

- Processes for the filing, retrieval, retention, archival, and disposal of records

- How data integrity is maintained throughout the life cycle of the data

Why is the control of records important?

- Evidence of activities performed

- Evidence of compliance with GMP requirements and company policies

- Procedures and work instructions

- Effectiveness of pharmaceutical QMS

- Traceability

- Process authenticity and consistency

- Evidence of the good quality attributes of the medicinal products manufactured

- In case of complaints, records could be used for investigational purposes

Managing and controlling master records are necessary to ensure the risk of someone inappropriately using and/or falsifying a record "by ordinary means" (that is, not requiring the use of specialist fraud skills) is reduced to an acceptable level.

There must be document controls in place to assure product quality. In the case of the United States, the FDA recommends that, if used, blank forms (including, but not limited to, worksheets, laboratory notebooks, and master production and control records) be controlled by the quality unit or by another document control method. For example, numbered sets of blank forms may be issued as appropriate and must be reconciled upon completion of all issued forms. Incomplete or erroneous forms must be kept as part of the permanent record along with written justification for their replacement. Similarly, bound paginated notebooks, stamped for official use by a document control group, allow detection of unofficial notebooks as well as of any gaps in notebook pages.

In general, companies must design and control their paper documentation systems to prevent the unauthorized recreation of GMP data. The template (blank) forms used for manual recordings may be created in an electronic system (Word, Excel, and so on). The corresponding master documents must be approved and controlled electronically or in paper versions. The following expectations must be considered for the template (blank) form:

- Have a unique reference number (including version number) and include reference to corresponding SOP number

- Must be stored in a manner that ensures appropriate version control

- If signed electronically, must use a secure e-signature

The distribution of template records ("blank" forms) must be controlled. The following expectations must be considered where appropriate, based on data risk and criticality:

- Enable traceability for issuance of the blank form by using a bound logbook with numbered pages or other appropriate system

- For loose-leaf template forms, the distribution date, a sequential issuing number, the number of the copies distributed, the department name where the blank forms are distributed, and any other necessary information must be documented

- Distributed copies must be designed to avoid duplication (photocopying) either by using a secure stamp or by using a paper color code not available in the working areas or another appropriate system

7.3 USE AND CONTROL OF MOVABLE STORAGE DEVICES

The use of uncontrolled external devices (external hard drives, USB drives, and so on) to store electronic data is a common finding during regulatory inspections. Common elements of those findings is the absolute lack of restriction to access files and information stored in them, allowing anyone to modify, delete, or add information. These failures to prevent unauthorized access or changes to data and to provide adequate controls to prevent manipulation and omission of data must be controlled by procedures. Laboratory and production computers must have their access port (USB) locked and only systems administrators have permission to unlock them to load or download information.

Following are three examples from FDA's warning letter citing this type of situation.

A warning letter[1] to an API manufacturer issued December 31, 2015, under "Access to information during inspection" stated:

We note that some records we requested during the inspection were not provided in a timely manner. During the inspection, an analyst removed a USB thumb drive from a computer controlling an HPLC. When asked to provide the drive, the analyst instead exited the room with the thumb drive. After approximately 15

---

[1]   https://www.fda.gov/ICECI/EnforcementActions/WarningLetters/ucm480035.htm. Accessed December 29, 2018.

minutes, management provided our investigator with what they asserted was the USB thumb drive in question. It is impossible to know whether management provided the same USB thumb drive that the analyst had removed.

When an owner, operator, or agent delays, denies, limits, or refuses an inspection, the drugs may be adulterated under section 501(j) of the FD&C Act. We recommend that you review FDA's guidance for industry *Circumstances that Constitute Delaying, Denying, Limiting, or Refusing a Drug Inspection.*

In another warning letter[2] dated May 14, 2018, the FDA cited:

Failure to exercise sufficient controls over computerized systems to prevent unauthorized access or changes to data, and failure to have adequate controls to prevent omission of data.

Our investigator found that audit trails in your standalone instruments ((b)(4) high-performance liquid chromatography systems, (b)(4) gas chromatography systems, and (b)(4) infrared radiation system) were not enabled. You also did not have other mechanisms for recording and monitoring any changes to data generated on these instruments. Your firm backed up electronic data from these instruments to a portable drive (b)(4). However, the drive was not password protected, and it was stored in an unlocked drawer in an unlocked office.

Finally, in a March 10, 2017, warning letter[3], the FDA cited:

3. Your firm failed to exercise appropriate controls over computer or related systems to assure that only authorized personnel institute changes in master production and control records, or other records (21 CFR 211.68(b)).

B. No restricted access to the microbial identification instrument. Further, you lacked restricted access to the external hard drive used for backup of this instrument. All users could delete or modify files.

---

[2] https://www.fda.gov/ICECI/EnforcementActions/WarningLetters/ucm608713.htm. Accessed December 29, 2018.
[3] https://www.fda.gov/ICECI/EnforcementActions/WarningLetters/2017/ucm546483.htm. Accessed December 29, 2018.

7.4 PERSONNEL ATTENDANCE RECORDS

Nowadays, practically 100% of regulated companies control the access to their premises, either electronically (employees using their ID card to open gates) or by manual signature for visitors. Entrance information becomes a critical piece of evidence during some investigations, and these data have, in the past, permitted regulatory authorities to demonstrate the falsification of records because the employee was out one specific date, although his/her signature appears the same date in records as performer or verifier of some GMP activities.

7.5 DATA INTEGRITY IN THE TRAINING AREA

Effective training of the workforce is one of the most basic and critical activities in which a regulated company must engage. Rampant falsification of training records to show passing results in the learning assessment process (typically an exam) or directly offering the exam with the answer prefilled are some of the situations frequently cited in regulatory inspections.

When you are auditing a regulated company and find hundreds of non-conformities with the combination of human error as root cause and retraining (or awareness, counseling, or a similar word) as the corrective action and then you review training records for those employees and the learning assessment was always 100%, something is wrong. Although most of the companies do not engage in rampant falsification nor provide prefilled exams, the administration of the exams during the learning assessment process typically lacks rigor. People shared comments and responses for the typically low complexity questions, and at the end, there are 100% perfect scores. This lack of seriousness can be considered as cheating too.

Following are two examples from FDA's warning letter regarding training controls:

In a warning letter[4] dated October 2015, the FDA cited:

3. Your firm failed to ensure that each person engaged in the manufacture, processing, packing, or holding of a drug product has the education, training, and experience, or any combination thereof,

---

4 https://www.fda.gov/ICECI/EnforcementActions/WarningLetters/2015/ucm474013.htm. Accessed December 29, 2018.

to enable that person to perform his or her assigned functions, and that training in current good manufacturing practice is conducted by qualified individuals (21 CFR 211.25(a)).

During interviews with our investigators, your contract employee who trains other contract employees on good documentation practices was unable to explain the material he was required to present during training. In addition, while a significant number of your contract employees do not speak English, you only provided English training materials to these employees.

We also found an employee's failing equipment qualification training assessment form in the trash, yet that employee's official file showed passing results. According to your company policies, personnel with failing scores must be retrained, but your firm was unable to provide evidence of retraining in the employee's official record.

According to your response of September 22, 2014, department heads are now responsible for training their contractors. Your response is inadequate, as you failed to assess how critical operations were affected by unqualified personnel.

You have not demonstrated that you have provided employees with appropriate resources and training to make sure that they are qualified for the operations they performed. Falsification and manipulation of employee training records is unacceptable.

In another egregious warning letter[5] dated July 2014, the FDA cited:

b. The inspection revealed that your firm falsified documents designed to demonstrate the effectiveness of cGMP training. Your production head admitted to pre-filling out the answers to post-training comprehension assessment questions and entering the names of employees on these documents. Your company policies require personnel to demonstrate understanding of training through evaluation.

That a senior manager was engaged in the falsification of documents is troubling and raises questions about validity of documents generated by your firm. Furthermore, your response to the FDA Form-483 is deficient in that it fails to address the root cause or the extent of the falsification of training documents. In response to this letter, provide this information and also indicate how your systems will be changed to address these fundamental issues.

---

[5] https://www.fda.gov/ICECI/EnforcementActions/WarningLetters/ucm409898.htm. Accessed December 29, 2018.

Provide a summary of your investigation into the training status of all employees participating in cGMP activities at your facility. As part of this overall training summary, include an update on the training of all contract employees. Also include your current curriculum for general cGMP training.

7.6 SELF-INSPECTIONS

The company's internal audit or self-assessment program must include data integrity as one of its main focuses. Most internal audit programs lack an adequate assessment of the integrity of the data and records that are generated to meet product and process requirements. As an example of the regulatory authorities' expectations for self-inspection/internal audit programs, during December 2013, UK's MHRA announced that pharmaceutical manufacturers, importers, and contract laboratories, as part of their self-inspection programs, must review the effectiveness of their governance systems to ensure data integrity and traceability. MHRA also states that this aspect would begin to be covered during inspections from the start of 2014, when reviewing the adequacy of self-inspection programs in accordance with Chapter 9 of the EU GMP. Finally, the UK agency mentioned that it is also expected that in addition to having their own governance systems, companies outsourcing activities should verify the adequacy of comparable systems at the contract acceptor.

Therefore, the expectations for the self-inspection program related to data integrity is that ongoing compliance with the company's data governance policy/procedures must be reviewed during self-inspection, to ensure they remain effective. This must also include elements of the data life cycle discussed in Chapter 6. Be sure to embed good documentation practices and data integrity verification in self-inspection processes.

In the quality control microbiology and analytical laboratories, the internal audit program must be looking at the security of the data, especially on standalone computers related to instruments that are not interfaced with a laboratory information management system. Among other things, be sure to verify the following:

- Are controls in place to ensure data are complete?

- Are activities documented at the time of performance?

- Are activities attributable to a specific individual?

- Can only authorized individuals make changes to records?

- Is there a record of changes to data?

- Are records reviewed for accuracy, completeness, and compliance with established standards?

- Are data maintained securely from data creation through disposition after the record's retention period?

- Are access control using unique usernames and passwords?

- Are privileges of each user consistent with his/her role?

- Is the administrator function independent of the systems?

- Are there audit trail activations?

- Who can deactivate the audit trail function?

- Are adequate samples of audit trails evaluated to identify manipulation or intent of manipulation?

- Are metadata evaluated from a sample of invalidate and nonconforming tests (out of specification [OOS] and out of trend [OOT])?

- Are laboratory logbooks (both paper and electronic if they exist, where laboratory personnel document significant activities such as reception of samples, monitoring activities, and so on) evaluated for out-of-sequence entries that might indicate noncontemporaneous documentation?

- Is the use of Post-it Notes or other unofficial documentation forms checked?

In production operations, the internal audit program must be looking, among other things, to the following:

- Contemporaneous recording of data (no backdating, no prerecorded information)

- Control of the issuance of records (batch records, forms used to record in-process sampling and/or testing, and so on)

- Use of Post-it Notes or other unofficial documentation

- Out-of-sequence logbook entries that might indicate noncontemporaneous documentation

- Employees signing off on activities they did not perform or witness

A few final suggestions when self-inspecting data integrity/good documentation practices:

- Train auditors using industry (from published inspectional findings) and in-house examples

- Perform unannounced audits and quality walks looking for ongoing records

- Spend time in the laboratory and manufacturing floor, including late shifts

- Focus on raw data handling and data review/verification

- Make good documentation practices and data integrity a permanent subject of GMP talks and refreshers

- Consider external support to avoid bias

Appendix C contains more than 100 ALCOA auditing/assessment questions for both paper and electronic documents and a basic guidance on how to classify those data integrity findings.

7.7 LABORATORY RECORDS

Laboratory records are second to none regarding lack of data integrity and good documentation practice issues. In one example, the FDA made the following citation in a March 2016 warning letter:[6]

3. Your firm failed to ensure that laboratory records included complete data derived from all tests necessary to assure compliance with established specifications and standards (21 CFR 211.194(a)).

During our inspection, we observed multiple examples of incomplete, inaccurate, or falsified laboratory records.

a. EM records for active air monitoring of the aseptic filling area reported samples as being collected when they were not actually collected, and some records documented purported EM results of zero colony forming units (CFU) even when the samples for which those results were reported were not actually collected. Contemporaneous video recordings that FDA reviewed during the inspection showed that such EM samples had not been collected, even though your laboratory records reported results for those samples. Our investigators observed your firm's practice of falsifying EM results for samples that were not collected for multiple

---

[6] https://www.fda.gov/iceci/enforcementactions/warningletters/2016/ucm489735.htm. Accessed December 29, 2018.

drugs, including (b)(4) injection USP lot (b)(4) and (b)(4) injection lot (b)(4).

Although your laboratory records for these products and lots indicated that you collected active air samples, the video we reviewed during the inspection demonstrated that operators did not actually collect the samples. During the inspection, your microbiologist confirmed that these EM samples were never collected. Additionally, two microbiologists informed the investigator that media plates were labeled and submitted for incubation as though they had been exposed to the environment. However, these media plates were never actually exposed to the environment. Your microbiologist indicated that this practice was routine and due to "work pressure." Because the EM results for samples were falsely reported as having been collected and/or as having produced no CFU growth, you lack assurance that the injectable drugs your firm produced in this area were sterile at the end of the aseptic filling process.

7.7.1 Exclusion of data for decision making

Data may only be invalidated and therefore excluded where it can be demonstrated through valid scientific justification that the data are not representative of the quantity measured, sampled, or acquired. In all cases, this justification must be documented and considered during data review and reporting. All data (even if excluded) must be retained with the original data set and be available for review in a format that allows the validity of the decision to exclude the data to be confirmed.

In the case of the U.S. FDA, its guidance for industry[7] "Investigating Out-of-Specification (OOS) Test Results for Pharmaceutical Production" refers to this topic under the "Outlier Tests" section.

The cGMP regulations require that statistically valid quality control criteria include appropriate acceptance and/or rejection levels (§ 211.165(d)). On rare occasions, a value may be obtained that is markedly different from the others in a series obtained using a validated method. Such a value may qualify as a statistical outlier. An outlier may result from a deviation from prescribed test methods, or it may be the result of variability in the sample. It should never be assumed that the reason for an outlier is error in the testing procedure, rather than inherent variability in the sample being tested.

---

[7] https://www.fda.gov/downloads/drugs/guidances/ucm070287.pdf. Accessed December 29, 2018.

Outlier testing is a statistical procedure for identifying from an array those data that are extreme. The possible use of outlier tests should be determined in advance. This should be written into SOPs for data interpretation and be well documented. The SOPs should include the specific outlier test to be applied with relevant parameters specified in advance. The SOPs should specify the minimum number of results required to obtain a statistically significant assessment from the specified outlier test.

For biological assays having a high variability, an outlier test may be an appropriate statistical analysis to identify those results that are statistically extreme observations. The USP describes outlier tests in the general chapter on *Design and Analysis of Biological Assays* <111>. In these cases, the outlier observation is omitted from calculations. The USP also states that "arbitrary rejection *or* retention of an apparently aberrant response can be a serious source of bias . . . the rejection of observations solely on the basis of their relative magnitudes is a procedure to be used sparingly" (USP <111>).

For validated chemical tests with relatively small variance, and if the sample being tested can be considered homogeneous (for example, an assay of a composite of a dosage form drug to determine strength), an outlier test is only a statistical analysis of the data obtained from testing and retesting. It will not identify the cause of an extreme observation and, therefore, should not be used to invalidate the suspect result. Occasionally, an outlier test may be of some value in estimating the probability that the OOS result is discordant from a data set, and this information can be used in an auxiliary fashion, along with all other data from the investigation, to evaluate the significance of the result.

Outlier tests have no applicability in cases where the variability in the product is what is being assessed, such as for content uniformity, dissolution, or release rate determinations. In these applications, a value perceived to be an outlier may in fact be an accurate result of a nonuniform product.

When using these practices during the additional testing performed in an OOS investigation, the laboratory will obtain multiple results. It is again critical for the laboratory to provide all test results for evaluation and consideration by the QCU in its final disposition decision. In addition, when investigation by a contract laboratory does not determine an assignable cause, all test results should be reported to the customer on the certificate of analysis.

In summary, any data created as part of a cGMP record must be evaluated by the quality unit as part of release criteria and maintained for cGMP purposes. Even if test results are legitimately invalidated on the basis of a scientifically sound investigation, the full cGMP batch record provided to the quality unit must include the original (invalidated) data, along with the investigation report that justifies invalidating the results. After a thorough investigation, a firm's quality unit might conclude that the initial OOS result did not reflect the true quality of the batch.

Electronic data generated to fulfill cGMP requirements must include all relevant metadata. To exclude data from the release criteria decision-making process, there must be a valid, documented, scientific justification for its exclusion. The requirements for record retention and review do not differ depending on the data format; paper-based and electronic data record-keeping systems are subject to the same requirements.

7.7.2 Review of laboratory records

Original laboratory records must be reviewed by a second person (§ 211.194 (a)(8)) to ensure all test results and associated information are appropriately reported. In other words, it is necessary that a second person verify the accuracy of all laboratory records. This requirement becomes ever more critical when test results are generated by instruments without printing capabilities. In those cases, the analyst contemporaneously documents the displayed results in the laboratory record (either paper of electronic), and it is imperative that a second person witness the process to ensure the accuracy of those document results.

Similarly, in microbiology, a contemporaneous written record is created of the colony counts of a Petri dish, and these results must be subject to second-person witnessing.

7.7.3 System suitability

Performing trial tests during system suitability or equilibration runs became one of the top observations from the FDA and worldwide regulators.

The FDA prohibits sampling and testing with the goal of achieving a specific result or to overcome an unacceptable result (for example, testing different samples until the desired passing result is obtained). This practice, also referred to as testing into compliance, is not consistent with cGMP. In some situations, use of actual samples to perform system suitability testing has been used as a means of testing into compliance. The FDA established in the 2016 draft guidance for data integrity that they would consider it a violative practice to use an actual sample in test, prep, or equilibration runs as a means of disguising testing into compliance.

According to the United States Pharmacopeia (USP), system suitability tests must include replicate injections of a standard preparation or other standard solutions to determine if requirements for precision are satisfied (see USP General Chapter <621> Chromatography). System suitability tests, including the identity of the preparation to be injected and the rationale for its selection, must be performed according to the firm's established written procedures and the approved application or applicable compendial monograph.

If an actual sample is to be used for system suitability testing, it must be a properly characterized secondary standard, written procedures must be established and followed, and the sample must be from a different batch than the sample(s) being tested. All data, including obvious error and failing, must be included in the cGMP records that are retained and subject to review. An investigation with objective evidence and a scientifically sound justification are necessary for data to be invalidated and excluded for the determination of conformance to specification for a batch.

Speaking in general terms, regulated companies must take precautions to discourage testing or processing data toward a desired outcome. For example:

- To minimize potential bias and ensure consistent data processing, test methods must have established sample acquisition and processing parameters, established in default version-controlled electronic acquisition and processing method files, as appropriate. Changes to these default parameters may be necessary during sample processing, but these changes must be documented (who, what, when?) and justified (why?).

- System suitability runs must include only established standards or reference materials of known concentration to provide an appropriate comparator for the potential variability of the instrument. If a sample (for example, a well-characterized secondary standard) is used for system suitability or a trial run, written procedures must be established and followed, and the results included in the data review process. The sample under test must not be used for trial run purposes or to evaluate suitability of the system.

Another unacceptable practice frequently found during inspection is that some companies only save the final results from reprocessed laboratory chromatography. Analytical methods must be capable and stable. For most laboratory analyses, reprocessing data must not be regularly needed.

If chromatography is reprocessed, written procedures must be established and followed, and each result retained for review. Good documentation practices and data integrity principles require complete data in laboratory records, which includes raw data, graphs, charts, and spectra from laboratory instruments.

7.8 PRODUCTION RECORDS

In an August 2016 warning letter[8] to a pharmaceutical company, the FDA cited the following:

1. Your firm failed to establish an adequate quality control unit with the responsibility and authority to approve or reject all components, drug product containers, closures, in-process materials, packaging material, labeling, and drug products (21 CFR 211.22(a)).

Your firm's quality unit allowed the use of adulterated (b)(4) USP API, dated May 25–31, 2015, manufactured at the Pan Drugs Nandesari facility. The Pan Drugs Nandesari facility was placed on FDA import alert 66-40 on May 5, 2015, for egregious cGMP deviations. Your firm used this API for the manufacture of (b)(4), which were then shipped to the U.S. market from October 7 to November 23, 2015.

Additionally, your quality unit approved certificates of analysis (CoA) for (b)(4) and (b)(4) API, as well as finished products, prior to conducting all quality control and release testing. Your production manager falsified the documents by signing and dating the "Prepared By" and "Checked By" sections of the COA.

Furthermore, your quality unit failed to identify data integrity issues in 11 batch production records reviewed by our investigator. Your production manager admitted that he falsified the signatures of other employees in the "Prepared By," "Reviewed By," "Approved By," and "Authorized By" sections.

According to your response, you recognized that these practices were not adequate. You intended to implement a signature list and revise your SOPs to address these failures. However, these actions do not address the quality unit failures observed.

---

[8] https://www.fda.gov/iceci/enforcementactions/warningletters/2016/ucm518540.htm. Accessed December 29, 2018.

In a June 2016 warning letter[9] to an API manufacturer, the FDA cited:

> 2. Failure to document manufacturing operations at the time they are performed.
>
> During the inspection, our investigator reviewed 20 executed batch manufacturing records and found that most of them contained similar or identical entries that could not be adequately explained. For example, our investigator examined batch records for (b)(4) different batches of (b)(4) API manufactured between January and February 2015. All (b)(4) batch records indicated that certain process steps or measurements had transpired at exactly the same time for each different batch. When our investigator asked your production supervisor to explain why the timestamps were identical on these records, the production supervisor stated that the full manufacturing process takes (b)(4) to complete, and that all batch records are kept in the production area until (b)(4) lots are completed. The production supervisor stated that the operators most likely did not record the actions at the time they were performed but rather completed batch records in groups.

7.8.1 Documentation and verification of activities

Following are some examples of unofficial documentation of GMP activities cited in a warning letter[10] issued by the FDA in December 2015:

> 3. Your firm failed to ensure that all quality-related activities are recorded at the time they are performed.
>
> Our inspection found that your firm's employees use "rough or unofficial notebooks" to document various cGMP activities. During their walk-through, our investigators found "unofficial" notebooks in the engineering office at your Zyfine (b)(4) plant, in the quality assurance office at your Zyfine (b)(4) plant, and in the scrap yard shared by (b)(4) plants.
>
> a. For example, an "unofficial" notebook found in the engineering office stated, "Pseudomonas present in (b)(4) water system" on November 26, 2014 and "(b)(4) water system (Activity) investigation" on November 25, 2014. Your firm was unable to pro-

---

[9]   https://www.fda.gov/iceci/enforcementactions/warningletters/2016/ucm508291.htm. Accessed December 29, 2018.

[10] https://www.fda.gov/ICECI/EnforcementActions/WarningLetters/2015/ucm479712 .htm. Accessed December 29, 2018.

vide the investigators with any documentation regarding *Pseudo-monas sp.* found in your water system and the related investigation.

In your response to the observation, you explained that this failure occurred during qualification of your water system, which was still in progress at the time of your response. Your response was deficient; the fact that your investigation into the presence of *Pseudomonas sp.* in your water system transpired during the qualification of that system is irrelevant. You must document all cGMP activities at the time you perform them, including equipment qualification and any deviations observed during such activities.

b. Our investigators found several plastic bags filled with paperwork and other scrapped items in the scrap yard. One item was a torn notebook of deficiencies recorded during review of your batch manufacturing records. For example, page 22 included a comment on batch **(b)(4)** "not mentioned any deviations of lower yield." Our review of the batch record **(b)(4)** found that the yield reported was **(b)(4)**% (range: **(b)(4)**%), but the batch record did not indicate a deviation.

In another warning letter[11] dated March 2016, the FDA cited:

Our investigators observed poor documentation practices during production and in-process testing.

i. Media fill batch (b)(4) documented a "check by" operation performed by an operator who was not present at the facility. This operator signed "checked by" for 63 out of (b)(4) individual (b)(4). In addition, during this media fill, a Quality Assurance (QA) individual signed "checked by" for observing the intervention "(b)(4) of conveyor belt" from (b)(4) to (b)(4) on December 2, 2014, but the QA individual was not present in the filling room when this intervention was performed, and did not view it.

7.8.2 Equipment alarms

A frequent source of significant data integrity findings is the evaluation by regulatory authorities of equipment alarms data. A typical computer system will have several built-in alarms to alert personnel to some out-of-limit situations or malfunctions. Inspectors will evaluate what specific functions are linked to alarms. For example, alarms may be linked to power supply

---

[11] https://www.fda.gov/iceci/enforcementactions/warningletters/2016/ucm489735.htm. Accessed December 29, 2018.

devices, feedback signals to confirm execution of commands, and operational process conditions such as empty or overflowing tanks.

The inspector might ask for the alarm thresholds for control of critical functions and whether such thresholds can be changed by the operator. For example, if the temperature of water in a process tank is linked to an alarm that sounds when the temperature drops below a specified temperature, can the operator change the threshold to another temperature?

How the company's employees respond when an alarm is activated must be covered in written operating procedures. In addition to the type of alarms (lights, buzzers, whistles, and so on), other important factors to consider are:

- How the company assures the proper performance of the alarm

- Are they tested periodically and equipped with in-line monitoring lights to show they are ready?

- How alarms are documented in production records, in separate logs or automatic electronic recording

- Can all alarm conditions be displayed simultaneously, or must they be displayed and responded to consecutively?

- If an employee is monitoring a display covering one phase of the operation, will that display alert the employee to an alarm condition at a different phase? If so, how?

- The operation of the computerized systems alarms must be validated as part of the complete computerized system under actual operating conditions

8

Clinical Data Integrity

8.1 ICH E6(R2) GOOD CLINICAL PRACTICE GUIDANCE

Good clinical practice (GCP) is an international ethical and scientific quality standard for designing, conducting, recording, and reporting trials that involve the participation of human subjects. Compliance with this standard provides public assurance that the rights, safety, and well-being of trial subjects are protected, consistent with the principles that have their origin in the Declaration of Helsinki, and that the clinical trial data are credible.

Harmonized guidance for good clinical practices is published by the International Conference on Harmonization (ICH) as part of the Efficacy guidance series. The objective of the ICH GCP guidance codified as E6 Good Clinical Practice[1] is to provide a unified standard for the European Union, Japan, and the United States to facilitate the mutual acceptance of clinical data by the regulatory authorities in these jurisdictions.

The original guidance E6(R1) Good Clinical Practice was developed by the ICH in 1996 with consideration of the current good clinical practices of the European Union, Japan, and the United States, as well as those of Australia, Canada, the Nordic countries, and the WHO. It described the responsibilities and expectations of all participants in the conduct of clinical trials, including investigators, monitors, sponsors, and Institutional Review Board (IRBs). GCP covers aspects of monitoring, reporting, and archiving of clinical trials.

This guidance must be followed when generating clinical trial data that are intended to be submitted to regulatory authorities. The principles established in this guidance may also be applied to other clinical investigations that may have an impact on the safety and well-being of human subjects.

---

[1] http://www.ich.org/fileadmin/Public_Web_Site/ICH_Products/Guidelines/Efficacy /E6/E6_R2__Step_4_2016_1109.PDF. Accessed December 15, 2018.

Regulatory authorities of many countries (ICH members in particular) adopted the original GCP guidelines in a formal manner without modification, while some others (such as India) adapted them significantly to align with local laws and subsequently published their own versions.

This harmonized guideline has been amended in 2016 by ICH with an integrated addendum to encourage implementation of improved and more efficient approaches to clinical trial design, conduct, oversight, recording, and reporting while continuing to ensure human subject protection and reliability of trial results. Standards regarding electronic records and essential documents intended to increase clinical trial quality and efficiency have also been updated. Risk management and quality of data-data integrity are the primal focus of the amended version.

The guidance addendum, referred to as E6(R2) Good Clinical Practice: Integrated Addendum to E6(R1), updates the previous version of the E6 guideline from 1996 and was adopted by the ICH Assembly in November 2016. Shortly after its adoption by ICH, the EMA finalized their version of the guideline, which came into effect for the EU in June 2017. Switzerland has also amended its Clinical Trials Ordinance to refer to E6(R2) as of May 1, 2017. The U.S. FDA adopted it in March 2018.

Since the development of the ICH GCP Guidance, the scale, complexity, and cost of clinical trials have increased. Evolutions in technology and risk management processes offer new opportunities to increase efficiency and focus on relevant activities. When the original ICH E6(R1) text was prepared, clinical trials were performed in a largely paper-based process. Advances in use of electronic data recording and reporting facilitate implementation of other approaches. For example, centralized monitoring can now offer a greater advantage, to a broader range of trials than is suggested in the original text. Therefore, this guidance has been amended to encourage implementation of improved and more efficient approaches to clinical trial design, conduct, oversight, recording, and reporting while continuing to ensure human subject protection and reliability of trial results. Standards regarding electronic records and essential documents intended to increase clinical trial quality and efficiency have also been updated.

8.1.1 GCP definitions

Following are some key definitions of ICH E6(R2) related to good documentation practices and/or data integrity.

Certified copy. A copy (irrespective of the type of media used) of the original record that has been verified (for example, by a dated signature or by generation through a validated process) to have the same information, including data that describe the context, content, and structure, as the original.

Documentation. All records, in any form (including, but not limited to, written, electronic, magnetic, and optical records, and scans, x-rays, and electrocardiograms) that describe or record the methods, conduct, and/or results of a trial, the factors affecting a trial, and the actions taken.

Good clinical practice. A standard for the design, conduct, performance, monitoring, auditing, recording, analyses, and reporting of clinical trials that provides assurance that the data and reported results are credible and accurate, and that the rights, integrity, and confidentiality of trial subjects are protected.

Source data. All information in original records and certified copies of original records of clinical findings, observations, or other activities in a clinical trial necessary for the reconstruction and evaluation of the trial. Source data are contained in source documents (original records or certified copies).

Source document. Original documents, data, and records (for example, hospital records, clinical and office charts, laboratory notes, memoranda, subjects' diaries or evaluation checklists, pharmacy dispensing records, recorded data from automated instruments, copies or transcriptions certified after verification as being accurate copies, microfiches, photographic negatives, microfilm or magnetic media, x-rays, subject files, and records kept at the pharmacy, at the laboratories, and at medicotechnical departments involved in the clinical trial).

Validation of computerized systems. A process of establishing and documenting that the specified requirements of a computerized system can be consistently fulfilled from design until decommissioning of the system or transition to a new system. The approach to validation must be based on a risk assessment that takes into consideration the intended use of the system and the potential of the system to affect human subject protection and reliability of trial results.

In Section 2 of the guidance, under "The Principles of ICH GCP," the guidance includes the following requirement:

> All clinical trial information must be recorded, handled, and stored in a way that allows its accurate reporting, interpretation, and verification. This principle applies to all records referenced in this guidance, irrespective of the type of media used.

The guidance includes requirements associated with good data management/data integrity for the following actors/elements of the clinical trials:

- Institutional review board/independent ethics committee (IRB/IEC)

- Investigator

- Sponsor

- Clinical trial protocols

- Investigator's brochure

8.2 INSTITUTIONAL REVIEW BOARD/INDEPENDENT ETHICS COMMITTEE

Records. The IRB/IEC must retain all relevant records (for example, written procedures, membership lists, lists of occupations/affiliations of members, submitted documents, minutes of meetings, and correspondence) for a period of at least three years after completion of the trial and make them available upon request from the regulatory authorities.

8.3 INVESTIGATOR

Under Section 4.2 (Adequate Resources), it establishes that the investigator is responsible for supervising any individual or party to whom the investigator delegates trial-related duties and functions conducted at the trial site. If the investigator/institution retains the services of any individual or party to perform trial-related duties and functions, the investigator/institution must ensure this individual or party is qualified to perform those trial-related duties and functions and must implement procedures to ensure the integrity of the trial-related duties and functions performed and any data generated.

Under Section 4.9 (Records and Reports), it establishes the ALCOA principles: "The investigator/institution must maintain adequate and accurate source documents and trial records that include all pertinent observations on each of the site's trial subjects. Source data must be attributable, legible, contemporaneous, original, accurate, and complete. Changes to source data must be traceable, must not obscure the original entry, and must be explained if necessary (for example, via an audit trail)."

In the same section, it also establishes that:

- The investigator must ensure the accuracy, completeness, legibility, and timeliness of the data reported to the sponsor in the CRFs and in all required reports.

- Data reported on the CRF, which are derived from source documents, must be consistent with the source documents or the discrepancies must be explained.

- Any change or correction to a CRF must be dated, initialed, and explained (if necessary) and must not obscure the original entry (for example, an audit trail must be maintained). This applies to both written and electronic changes or corrections. Sponsors must provide guidance to investigators and/or the investigators' designated representatives on making such corrections. Sponsors must have written procedures to ensure that changes or corrections in CRFs made by sponsor's designated representatives are documented, are necessary, and are endorsed by the investigator. The investigator must retain records of the changes and corrections.

- The investigator/institution must maintain the trial documents as specified in Essential Documents for the Conduct of a Clinical Trial (see Section 8 of the guidance) and as required by the applicable regulatory requirement(s). The investigator/institution must take measures to prevent accidental or premature destruction of these documents.

- Essential documents must be retained until at least two years after the last approval of a marketing application in an ICH region and until there are no pending or contemplated marketing applications in an ICH region or until at least two years have elapsed since the formal discontinuation of clinical development of the investigational product. These documents must be retained for a longer period, however, if required by the applicable regulatory requirements or by an agreement with the sponsor. It is the responsibility of the sponsor to inform the investigator/institution as to when these documents no longer need to be retained.

8.4 SPONSOR

Under Section 5.0 (Quality Management), the guidance establishes that the sponsor must implement a system to manage quality throughout all stages of the trial process.

- Sponsors must focus on trial activities essential to ensuring human subject protection and the reliability of trial results. Quality management includes the design of efficient clinical trial protocols, tools, and procedures for data collection and processing, as well as the collection of information that is essential to decision making.

- The methods used to ensure and control the quality of the trial must be proportionate to the risks inherent in the trial and the importance of the information collected. The sponsor must ensure all aspects of the trial are operationally feasible and must avoid unnecessary complexity, procedures, and data collection. Protocols, CRFs, and other operational documents must be clear, concise, and consistent.

The guidance requires that the quality management system must use a risk-based approach as described below:

- Critical process and data identification—During protocol development, the sponsor must identify those processes and data that are critical to ensure human subject protection and the reliability of trial results.

- Risk identification—The sponsor must identify risks to critical trial processes and data. Risks must be considered at both the system level (for example, standard operating procedures, computerized systems, and personnel) and clinical trial level (for example, trial design, data collection, and informed consent process).

- Risk evaluation—The sponsor must evaluate the identified risks, against existing risk controls, by considering:

a. The likelihood of errors occurring

b. The extent to which such errors would be detectable

c. The impact of such errors on human subject protection and reliability of trial results

- Risk control—The sponsor must decide which risks to reduce and/ or which risks to accept. The approach used to reduce risk to an acceptable level must be proportionate to the significance of the risk. Risk reduction activities may be incorporated in protocol design and implementation, monitoring plans, agreements between parties defining roles and responsibilities, systematic safeguards to ensure adherence to standard operating procedures, and training in processes and procedures.

     Predefined quality tolerance limits must be established, taking into consideration the medical and statistical characteristics of the variables as well as the statistical design of the trial, to identify systematic issues that can impact subject safety or reliability of trial results. Detection of deviations from the predefined quality tolerance limits must trigger an evaluation to determine if action is needed.

- Risk communication—The sponsor must document quality management activities. The sponsor must communicate quality management activities to those who are involved in or affected by such activities, to facilitate risk review and continual improvement during clinical trial execution.

- Risk review—The sponsor must periodically review risk control measures to ascertain whether the implemented quality management activities remain effective and relevant, taking into account emerging knowledge and experience.

- Risk reporting—The sponsor must describe the quality management approach implemented in the trial and summarize important deviations from the predefined quality tolerance limits and remedial actions taken in the clinical study report (ICH E3, Section 9.6 Data Quality Assurance).

Under Section 5.1 (Quality Assurance and Quality Control), it establishes that:

- The sponsor is responsible for implementing and maintaining quality assurance and quality control systems with written SOPs to ensure trials are conducted and data are generated, documented (recorded), and reported in compliance with the protocol, GCP, and the applicable regulatory requirement(s)

- The sponsor is responsible for securing agreement from all involved parties to ensure direct access to all trial-related sites, source data/documents, and reports for the purpose of monitoring and auditing by the sponsor, and inspection by domestic and foreign regulatory authorities

- Quality control must be applied to each stage of data handling to ensure that all data are reliable and have been processed correctly

- Agreements, made by the sponsor with the investigator/institution and any other parties involved with the clinical trial, must be in writing, as part of the protocol or in a separate agreement

Under Section 5.2 (Contract Research Organization [CRO]), it establishes that:

- A sponsor may transfer any or all of the sponsor's trial-related duties and functions to a CRO, but the ultimate responsibility for the quality and integrity of the trial data always resides with the sponsor. The CRO must implement quality assurance and quality control.

- Any trial-related duty and function that is transferred to and assumed by a CRO must be specified in writing.

Under Section 5.5 (Trial Management, Data Handling, and Record-keeping), the guidance establishes that:

- The sponsor must utilize appropriately qualified individuals to supervise the overall conduct of the trial, to handle the data, to verify the data, to conduct the statistical analyses, and to prepare the trial reports.

- The sponsor may consider establishing an independent data monitoring committee (IDMC) to assess the progress of a clinical trial, including the safety data and the critical efficacy endpoints at intervals, and to recommend to the sponsor whether to continue, modify, or stop a trial. The IDMC must have written operating procedures and maintain written records of all its meetings.

- When using electronic trial data handling and/or remote electronic trial data systems, the sponsor must:

  a. Ensure and document that the electronic data processing system(s) conforms to the sponsor's established requirements for completeness, accuracy, reliability, and consistent intended performance (for example, validation). The sponsor must base their approach to validation of such systems on a risk assessment that takes into consideration the intended use of the system and the potential of the system to affect human subject protection and reliability of trial results.

  b. Maintains SOPs for using these systems. The SOPs must cover system setup, installation, and use. The SOPs must describe system validation and functionality testing, data collection and handling, system maintenance, system security measures, change control, data backup, recovery, contingency planning, and decommissioning. The responsibilities of the sponsor, investigator, and other parties with respect to the use of these computerized systems must be clear, and the users must be provided with training in their use.

  c. Ensure the systems are designed to permit data changes in such a way that the data changes are documented and that there is no deletion of entered data (for example, maintain an audit trail, data trail, edit trail).

  d. Maintain a security system that prevents unauthorized access to the data.

e. Maintain a list of the individuals who are authorized to make data changes.

f. Maintain adequate backup of the data.

g. Safeguard the blinding, if any (for example, maintain the blinding during data entry and processing).

h. Ensure the integrity of the data, including any data that describe the context, content, and structure. This is particularly important when making changes to the computerized systems, such as software upgrades or migration of data.

- If data are transformed during processing, it must always be possible to compare the original data and observations with the processed data.

- The sponsor must use an unambiguous subject identification code that allows identification of all the data reported for each subject.

- The sponsor, or other owners of the data, must retain all of the sponsor-specific essential documents pertaining to the trial. See Section 8 (Essential Documents for the Conduct of a Clinical Trial).

- The sponsor must retain all sponsor-specific essential documents in conformance with the applicable regulatory requirement(s) of the country or countries where the product is approved, and/or where the sponsor intends to apply for approval(s).

- If the sponsor discontinues the clinical development of an investigational product (i.e., for any or all indications, routes of administration, or dosage forms), the sponsor must maintain all sponsor-specific essential documents for at least two years after formal discontinuation or in conformance with the applicable regulatory requirement(s).

- If the sponsor discontinues the clinical development of an investigational product, the sponsor must notify all the trial investigators/institutions and all the regulatory authorities.

- Any transfer of ownership of the data must be reported to the appropriate authority or authorities, as required by the applicable regulatory requirement(s).

- The sponsor-specific essential documents must be retained until at least two years after the last approval of a marketing application in an ICH region and until there are no pending or contemplated marketing applications in an ICH region or until at least two years have elapsed since the formal discontinuation of clinical development of the investigational product. These documents must be retained for a longer period, however, if required by the applicable regulatory requirement(s) or if needed by the sponsor.

- The sponsor must inform the investigator(s)/institution(s) in writing of the need for record retention and must notify the investigator(s)/institution(s) in writing when the trial-related records are no longer needed.

Under Section 5.15 (Record Access), the guidance states that the sponsor must ensure it is specified in the protocol or other written agreement that the investigator(s)/institution(s) provide direct access to source data/documents for trial-related monitoring, audits, IRB/IEC review, and regulatory inspection.

Under Section 5.18 (Monitoring), the guidance establishes that the purposes of trial monitoring are to verify:

a. The rights and well-being of human subjects are protected

b. The reported trial data are accurate, complete, and verifiable from source documents.

c. The conduct of the trial is in compliance with the currently approved protocol/amendment(s), with GCP, and with the applicable regulatory requirement(s)

And under Extent and Nature of Monitoring, it requires:

- The sponsor must develop a systematic, prioritized, risk-based approach to monitoring clinical trials. The flexibility in the extent and nature of monitoring described in this section is intended to permit varied approaches that improve the effectiveness and efficiency of monitoring. The sponsor may choose onsite monitoring, a combination of onsite and centralized monitoring, or, where justified, centralized monitoring. The sponsor must document the rationale for the chosen monitoring strategy (for example, in the monitoring plan).

- Onsite monitoring is performed at the sites at which the clinical trial is being conducted. Centralized monitoring is a remote evaluation of accumulating data, performed in a timely manner, supported by appropriately qualified and trained persons (for example, data managers, biostatisticians).

- Centralized monitoring processes provide additional monitoring capabilities that can complement and reduce the extent and/or frequency of onsite monitoring and help distinguish between reliable data and potentially unreliable data. Review that may include statistical analyses of accumulating data from centralized monitoring can be used to:

    a. Identify missing data, inconsistent data, data outliers, unexpected lack of variability, and protocol deviations

    b. Examine data trends such as the range, consistency, and variability of data within and across sites

    c. Evaluate for systematic or significant errors in data collection and reporting at a site or across sites; or potential data manipulation or data integrity problems

    d. Analyze site characteristics and performance metrics

    e. Select sites and/or processes for targeted onsite monitoring.

- Monitor's responsibilities include checking the accuracy and completeness of the CRF entries, source documents, and other trial-related records against each other. The monitor specifically must verify:

    i. The data required by the protocol are reported accurately on the CRFs and are consistent with the source documents

- Monitoring plan—The sponsor must develop a monitoring plan that is tailored to the specific human subject protection and data integrity risks of the trial. The plan must describe the monitoring strategy, the monitoring responsibilities of all the parties involved, the various monitoring methods to be used, and the rationale for their use. The plan must also emphasize the monitoring of critical data and processes. Particular attention must be given to those aspects that are not routine clinical practice and that require additional training. The monitoring plan must reference the applicable policies and procedures.

8.5 CLINICAL TRIAL PROTOCOL

The guidance establishes the general content of a trial protocol including amendment(s), if necessary. Among those are the data-keeping elements that must be part of the protocol design. As explained across the guidance, good data management (good documentation practices, data integrity, and so on) are primal consideration and foundation principles of good clinical practices.

8.6 INVESTIGATOR BROCHURE

The investigator's brochure (IB) is a compilation of the clinical and nonclinical data on the investigational product(s) that are relevant to the study of the product(s) in human subjects. Its purpose is to provide the investigators and others involved in the trial with the information to facilitate their understanding of the rationale for, and their compliance with, many key features of the protocol, such as the dose, dose frequency/interval, methods of administration, and safety-monitoring procedures.

This guidance delineates the minimum information that must be included in an IB and provides suggestions for its layout.

Generally, the sponsor is responsible for ensuring an up-to-date IB is made available to the investigator(s) and the investigators are responsible for providing the up-to-date IB to the responsible IRBs/IECs.

Under Section 7.3 (Contents of the Investigator's Brochure), the guidance requires a "Summary of Data and Guidance for the Investigator," including an overall discussion of the nonclinical and clinical data and must summarize the information from various sources on different aspects of the investigational product(s), wherever possible. In this way, the investigator can be provided with the most informative interpretation of the available data and with an assessment of the implications of the information for future clinical trials.

9

Preventing Data Integrity Problems

9.1 COMMITMENT FROM ALL: CREATING THE RIGHT ENVIRONMENT

Data integrity enables good decision making by manufacturers and regulatory authorities. It is a fundamental mandatory requirement of the medical product quality system, applying equally to manual (paper) and electronic systems. To ensure data integrity, senior management must engage in the promotion of a quality culture along with the implementation of appropriate organizational and technical controls. It requires participation and commitment by staff at all levels within the organization, by the organization's suppliers, and by its distributors.

Data integrity is a basic element of good documentation practices, one of the most fundamental pillars of any quality management system, including cGMP. Upper management, and especially quality leaders at every regulated organization, must ensure everyone is accountable for their actions, including having proper documentation of activities performed. Unfortunately, most regulated organizations only react to data integrity issues after regulators discover them.

An outrageous example of this can be found in a warning letter[1] issued in July 2014 in which the FDA required an organization to "identify the specific managers in place who participated in, facilitated, encouraged, or failed to stop subordinates from falsifying data in cGMP records, and determine the extent of top and middle management's involvement in or awareness of data manipulation." In the same inspection, the FDA also discovered that "your firm falsified documents designed to demonstrate the effectiveness of cGMP training. . . . That a senior manager was engaged in

---

[1]   https://www.fda.gov/ICECI/EnforcementActions/WarningLetters/2014/ucm409898 .htm. Accessed December 29, 2018.

the falsification of documents is troubling and raises questions about validity of documents generated by your firm."

Senior management, especially those with quality management responsibilities, must ensure data integrity risk is assessed, mitigated, and communicated in accordance with the principles of quality risk management. The effort and resources assigned to data integrity measures must be commensurate with the risk to product quality and balanced with other QA resource demands. Where long-term measures are identified to achieve the desired state of control, interim measures must be implemented to mitigate risk and must be monitored for effectiveness.

9.2 QUALITY CULTURE

Quality culture can be defined as "the collection of values, beliefs, thinking, and behaviors demonstrated consistently by management, team leaders, quality personnel, and all personnel that contribute to creating a quality culture to assure data integrity."

Management, with the support of the quality unit, must establish and maintain a working environment that minimizes the risk of noncompliant records and erroneous records and data. An essential element of the quality culture is the transparent and open reporting of deviations, errors, omissions, and aberrant results at all levels of the organization, irrespective of hierarchy. Steps must be taken to prevent and to detect and correct weaknesses in systems and procedures that may lead to data errors to continually improve the robustness of scientific decision making within the organization. Senior management must actively discourage any management practices that might reasonably be expected to inhibit the active and complete reporting of such issues, for example, hierarchical constraints and blame cultures.

Management must aim to create a work environment (quality culture) that is transparent and open, one in which personnel are encouraged to freely communicate failures and mistakes, including potential data reliability issues, so corrective and preventative actions can be taken. Organizational reporting structures must permit the information flow between personnel at all levels.

Management can foster quality culture in many ways. Among them:

- Ensure awareness and understanding of expectations (code of ethics and code of conduct)

- Lead by example; management must demonstrate the behaviors they expect to see

- Ensure accountability for actions and decisions

- Stay continuously and actively involved

- Set realistic expectations; consider the limitations that place pressures on employees

- Allocate resources to meet expectations

- Implement fair and just consequences and rewards

- Be aware of regulatory trends to apply lessons learned to your organization

An understanding of how behavior influences: (1) the incentive to amend, delete, or falsify data; and (2) the effectiveness of procedural controls designed to ensure data integrity can provide useful indicators of risks.

An effective quality culture and data governance may be different in its implementation from one company to another, and even from a company location to another. Depending on culture, an organization's control measures may be:

- **Open** (where hierarchy can be challenged by subordinates, and full reporting of a systemic or individual failure is a business expectation) or

- **Closed** (where reporting failure or challenging a hierarchy is culturally more difficult)

Good data governance in "open" cultures may be facilitated by employee empowerment to identify and report issues through the quality system. In "closed" cultures, a greater emphasis on oversight and secondary review may be required to achieve an equivalent level of control due to the social barrier of communicating undesirable information. The availability of anonymous escalation to senior management may also be of greater importance in this situation.

The extent of management's knowledge and understanding of data integrity can influence the organization's success of data integrity management. Management must know their legal and moral obligation (such as duty and power) to prevent data integrity lapses from occurring and to detect them, if they must occur.

Lapses in data integrity are not limited to fraud or falsification. They can be unintentional and still pose risk. Any potential for compromising the reliability of data is a risk that must be identified and understood for appropriate controls to be put in place. Direct controls usually take the form of written policies and procedures, but indirect influences on employee behavior (such as incentives for productivity in excess of process capability) must be understood and addressed as well.

Data integrity breaches can occur at any time and be caused by any employee, so management needs to be vigilant in detecting issues and understand reasons behind lapses, when found, to enable investigation of the issue and implementation of corrective and preventative actions.

There are consequences of data integrity lapses that affect the various stakeholders (patients, regulators, customers), including directly impacting patient safety and undermining confidence in the organization and its products. Employee awareness and understanding of these consequences can be helpful in fostering an environment in which quality is a priority.

Management must establish controls to prevent, detect, and correct data integrity breaches, as well as verify those controls are performing as intended to assure data integrity.

9.2.1 Code of ethics

A code of values and ethics must reflect management's philosophy on quality, achieved through policies (for example, a code of conduct) that are aligned to the quality culture and develop an environment of trust, where all individuals are responsible and accountable for ensuring patient safety and product quality. The company's general ethics and integrity standards need to be established and known to each employee, and these expectations must be communicated frequently and consistently.

Management must make personnel aware of the importance of their role in ensuring data integrity and the implication of their activities to assuring product quality and protecting patient safety.

Code of conduct policies must clearly define the expectation of ethical behavior, such as honesty. This must be communicated to and be well understood by all personnel. The communication must not be limited only to knowing the requirements, but must also include why they were established and the consequences of failing to fulfill the requirements. Unwanted behaviors, such as deliberate data falsification, unauthorized changes, destruction of data, or other conduct that compromises data integrity, must be addressed promptly. Disciplinary action may be taken, when warranted. Similarly, conforming behaviors must be recognized appropriately.

There must be a confidential escalation program supported by company policy and procedures whereby it encourages personnel to bring instances of possible breaches to the code of conduct to the attention of management without consequence.

9.3 MODERNIZING THE QUALITY MANAGEMENT SYSTEM

The application of modern quality risk management principles and good data management practices to the current medical products' quality management system serves to modernize the system to meet the challenges that come with the generation of complex data.

Every company's quality management system must be able to prevent, detect, and correct weaknesses in the system or their processes that may lead to data integrity lapses. The company must know its data life cycle and integrate the appropriate controls and procedures such that the data generated will be valid, complete, and reliable. Specifically, such control and procedural changes may be in the following areas:

- Risk assessment and management

- Investigation programs

- Data review practices

- Computer software validation

- Vendor/contractor management

- Training program to include company's data integrity policy and data integrity SOPs

- Self-inspection program to include data integrity

- Quality metrics and reporting to senior management

There must be regular management reviews of quality metrics, including those related to data integrity, such that significant issues are identified, escalated, and addressed in a timely manner. Caution must be taken when key performance indicators are selected so as not to inadvertently result in a culture in which data integrity is lower in priority. The head of the quality unit must have direct access to the highest level of management in order to directly communicate risks so that senior management is aware and can allocate resources to address any issues. Management can have an independent expert periodically verify the effectiveness of their systems and controls.

9.4 RESOURCES

Management must allocate appropriate resources to support and sustain good data integrity management such that the workload and pressures on those responsible for data generation and record keeping do not increase the likelihood of errors or the opportunity to deliberately compromise data integrity. Senior site management has the ultimate responsibility to ensure an effective quality management system is in place and that the responsibilities placed on any one individual should not be so extensive as to present any risk to quality.

There must be a sufficient number of personnel for quality and management oversight, IT support, conduct of investigations, and management of training programs that are commensurate with the operations of the organization. There must be provisions to purchase equipment, software, and hardware that are appropriate for their needs, based on the criticality of the data in question. Personnel must be qualified and trained for their specific duties, with appropriate segregation of duties, including the importance of good documentation practices. There must be evidence of the effectiveness of training on critical procedures, such as electronic data review. The concept of data integrity applies to all functional departments that play a role in GMP, including areas such as IT and engineering.

Data integrity must be familiar to all, but data integrity experts from various levels (subject-matter experts, supervisors/managers, and team leaders, among others) may be called upon to work together to conduct/support investigations, identify system gaps, and drive implementation of improvements. Introduction of new roles in an organization relating to data integrity such as a data custodian or chief compliance officer might be considered.

9.5 DATA INTEGRITY ISSUES AND HUMAN ERROR

Data integrity is a critical element of an organization's quality program. Reducing the risk for human error in our manufacturing and laboratory processes will ensure we comply with data integrity laws and regulations while building quality into our everyday practices and keeping the quality and safety of our products.

Regulators and quality auditors do not distinguish between human error or sloppiness, and data falsifications and fraud, when assessing the impact of data integrity failures, as demonstrated in the following excerpt from a 2015 FDA warning letter:[2]

> In correspondence with the agency, you indicate that no malicious data integrity patterns and practices were found. Also, you state that no intentional activity to disguise, misrepresent, or replace failing data with passing data was identified and no evidence of file deletion or manipulation was found. Your response and comments focus primarily on the issue of intent, and do not adequately address the seriousness of the cGMP violations found during the inspection.

If you are responsible for investigating some data integrity situation or for answering an inspection observation related to it, my recommendation is do not place all your emphasis explaining or justifying the absence of malicious data integrity pattern or falsification. Orient your regulatory energy into identifying and implementing good data controls that were missing or just failed.

---

[2] https://www.fda.gov/ICECI/EnforcementActions/WarningLetters/2015/ucm432709.htm. Accessed December 29, 2018.

10

Data Governance and Data Integrity Audit

10.1 WHAT IS DATA GOVERNANCE?

Data governance is the totality of arrangements to ensure data, irrespective of the format in which they are generated, are recorded, processed, retained, and used to ensure a complete, consistent, and accurate record throughout the data life cycle.

Data governance must address data ownership and accountability throughout the life cycle and consider the design, operation, and monitoring of processes/systems to comply with the principles of data integrity, including control over intentional and unintentional changes to data.

A critical success factor for data governance systems is the staff training in the importance of data integrity principles and the creation of a working environment that enables visibility and actively encourages reporting of errors, omissions, and undesirable results. Management must also make staff aware of the importance of their role in protecting the safety of patients and the reputation of their organization for quality products and services.

Management must create a work environment in which staff are encouraged to communicate failures and mistakes, including data reliability issues, so corrective and preventive actions can be taken and the quality of an organization's products and services are enhanced. This includes ensuring adequate information flow between staff at all levels. Senior management must actively discourage any management practices that might reasonably be expected to inhibit the active and complete reporting of such issues (for example, hierarchical constraints and blame cultures).

Senior management must be accountable for the implementation of systems and procedures to minimize the potential risk to data integrity. Senior management has the ultimate responsibility for ensuring an effective quality system is in place to achieve the quality objectives, and that staff roles, responsibilities, and authorities, including those required for effective data governance programs, are defined, communicated, and implemented throughout the organization. Leadership is essential to establish and maintain a company-wide commitment to data reliability as an essential element of the quality system.

Elements of effective management governance must include:

- Application of modern QRM principles and good data management principles that ensure the validity, completeness, and reliability of data

- Application of appropriate quality metrics

- Assurance that personnel are not subject to organizational pressures or incentives that may adversely affect the quality and integrity of their work

- Allocation of adequate human and technical resources such that the workload, work hours, and pressures on those responsible for data generation and record keeping do not increase errors

- Ensuring staff are aware of the importance of their role in ensuring data integrity and the relationship of these activities to assuring product quality and protecting patient safety

For contracted operations, contract givers must ensure data ownership, governance, and accessibility are included in any contract/technical agreement with a third party. The contract giver must also perform a data governance review as part of their vendor assurance program.

10.2 DATA GOVERNANCE SYSTEM REVIEW

The effectiveness of data integrity control measures must be assessed periodically as part of self-inspection (internal audit) or other periodic review processes. This must ensure that controls over the data life cycle are operating as intended. In addition to routine data verification checks, self-inspection activities must be extended to a wider review of control measures, including:

- A check of continued personnel understanding of data integrity in the context of protecting the patient and ensuring the maintenance of a working environment that is focused on quality and open reporting of issues (for example, by review of continued training in data integrity principles and expectations)

- A review for consistency of reported data/outcomes against raw data entries

- In situations where routine computerized system data is reviewed by a validated "exception report," a risk-based sample of computerized system logs/audit trails to ensure information of relevance to GMP activity is reported as expected

An effective review process will demonstrate understanding regarding importance of interaction of company behaviors with organizational and technical controls. The outcome of data governance system reviews must be communicated to senior management and be used in the assessment of residual data integrity risk.

Management reviews and regular reporting of quality metrics facilitate meeting these objectives. These must include metrics related to data integrity that will help identify opportunities for improvement. For example:

- Tracking and trending of invalid and aberrant data may reveal unforeseen variability in processes and procedures previously believed to be robust, opportunities to enhance analytical procedures and their validation, validation of processes, training of personnel, or sourcing of raw materials and components, among other situations.

- Adequate review of audit trails, including those reviewed as part of key decision-making steps (for example, batch release, issuance of a GLP study report, or approval of CRFs), may reveal incorrect processing of data, help prevent incorrect results from being reported, and identify the need for additional training of personnel.

- Routine audits and/or self-inspections of computerized systems may reveal gaps in security controls that inadvertently allow personnel to access and potentially alter time/date stamps. Such findings help raise awareness among management of the need to allocate resources to improve validation controls for computerized systems.

- Monitoring of contract acceptors and tracking and trending of associated quality metrics for these sites help to identify risks that may indicate the need for more active engagement and allocation of additional resources by the contract giver to ensure quality standards are met.

10.3 GOOD DOCUMENTATION PRACTICES AND DATA INTEGRITY SELF-INSPECTION AND SUPPLIER AUDITS

Self-inspections (internal audits), supplier audits, and risk reviews must identify and inform management of opportunities to improve foundational systems and processes that have an impact on data reliability. Allocation of resources by management to these improvements of systems and processes may efficiently reduce data integrity risks. For example, identifying and addressing technical difficulties with the equipment used to perform multiple GXP operations may greatly improve the reliability of data for all these operations. Another example relates to identifying conflicts of interests affecting security. Allocating independent technical support personnel to perform systems administration for computerized systems, including managing security, backup, and archiving, reduces potential conflicts of interest and may greatly streamline and improve data management efficiency.

All GXP records held by the GXP organization are subject to inspection by the responsible health authorities. This includes original electronic data and metadata, such as audit trails maintained in computerized systems. Management of both contract givers and contract acceptors must ensure adequate resources are available and procedures for computerized systems are available for inspection. Systems administrator personnel must be available to readily retrieve requested records and facilitate inspections.

The audit of the data governance system must ensure controls over data life cycle are established, implemented, and maintained. These controls must be commensurate with the principles of quality risk management. These controls may include:

Organizational controls

- The company's arrangements for data governance must be documented within the quality management system and regularly reviewed

- Policies, procedures, work instructions, and records (for example, procedures containing instructions for completion of records and retention of completed paper records)

- Effective training of all staff and documented authorization for data generation and approval

- Data governance system design, considering how data are generated, recorded, processed, retained, and used and how risks or vulnerabilities are controlled effectively

- Routine data verification

- Periodic surveillance (for example, self-inspection processes seek to verify the effectiveness of the data governance policy)

Technical control

- Computerized system control

- Automation

Denoting the importance of those auditing activities, the U.S. FDA allocated to the review of data integrity one of the three goals the agency established during the drug's preapproval inspection process. These three goals are:

- Whether the site has a quality system that is designed to achieve sufficient control over the facility and commercial manufacturing operations

- That the formulation, manufacturing, or processing methods, and analytical (or examination) methods, are consistent with descriptions contained in the application for the biobatch (and other pivotal clinical batches, when applicable), the proposed commercial scale batch, and the API(s)

- Integrity of raw data and all relevant data

Specifically, the objective 3 "Data Integrity Audit" establishes the following:

Audit the raw data, hardcopy or electronic, to authenticate the data submitted in the CMC section of the application. Verify that all relevant data (e.g., stability, biobatch data) were submitted in the CMC section such that CDER product reviewers can rely on the submitted data as complete and accurate.

Details regarding the preapproval inspection process are included in Section 4.2.3.

Our final recommendations regarding auditing of data integrity are:

- Always include data integrity elements in every quality system audit, including both internal and supplier ones.

- Include "data integrity" as a new element on your internal audit schedule. This way you'll verify data integrity elements during each audit and, additionally, you will have an audit solely focused on this critical element.

Appendix A includes a list of topics to be used during the assessment of data integrity controls.

11

Good Documentation Practices and Data Integrity Training

11.1 TRAINING FOR PROPER EXECUTION

All personnel working under a GXP environment must be trained in data integrity policies and procedures and agree to abide by them. Management must ensure that personnel are trained to understand and distinguish between proper and improper conduct, including deliberate falsification, and must be made aware of the potential consequences. Procedures such as good documentation practices (see Chapter 2.3) must be fully deployed and proper execution must be continually monitored.

Management must also ensure that, at the time of hire and periodically afterward, as needed, all personnel are trained in procedures to ensure good documentation practices for both paper and electronic records. The quality unit must include checks for adherence to good documentation practices for both paper records and electronic records in their day-to-day work, system and facility audits, and self-inspections and report any opportunities for improvement to management.

11.2 TRAINING FOR DETECTION OF DATA INTEGRITY ISSUES

All personnel must be trained in detecting data integrity issues as part of a routine cGMP training program. In the case of the U.S. FDA, training personnel to detect data integrity issues is consistent with the personnel requirements under § 211.25 and 212.10, which state that personnel must have the education, training, and experience, or any combination thereof, to perform their assigned duties. In the EMA and PIC/S requirements, Chapter 2 Personnel, under Section 2.10, establishes that "the manufacturer should provide training for all the personnel whose duties take them into production and storage areas or into control laboratories (including the technical, maintenance, and cleaning personnel), and for other personnel whose activities could affect the quality of the product."

In addition, key personnel, including managers, supervisors, and quality unit personnel, must be trained in specific measures to prevent and detect data integrity issues. This may require specific training in evaluating the configuration settings and reviewing electronic data and metadata, such as audit trails, for individual computerized systems used in the generation, processing, and reporting of data. For example:

- The quality unit must learn how to evaluate configuration settings that may intentionally or unintentionally allow data to be overwritten or obscured through the use of hidden fields or data annotation tools

- Supervisors responsible for reviewing electronic data must learn which audit trails in the system track significant data changes and how these might be most efficiently accessed as part of their review

An example of a comprehensive data integrity training certification is included in Appendix B.

12

Investigating and Disclosing Data Integrity Issues

12.1 INVESTIGATING DATA INTEGRITY ISSUES

Let's make clear from the onset: data integrity issues are important quality issues, not just problems for human resources department to fix, and they must be fully investigated under the cGMP quality system. They must be handled as any deviation would be, according to company's procedures.

Most companies are not dealing properly with these issues because typically the investigation is led by a human resource area without full involvement from the quality organization. Once you discover or detect a real or potential data integrity issue, open a formal investigation on whatever deviation documentation system you're using. The timely inclusion of any data integrity issue on your documented cGMP quality system will be a good sign for inspectors regarding your organization's compromise to timely address those issues.

When issues with data validity and reliability are discovered, it is important that their potential impact on patient safety and product quality and on the reliability of information used for decision making and applications is examined as a top priority. Regulatory authorities must be notified if the investigation identifies an impact on patients, products, reported information, or application dossiers.

As the FDA established in the 2018 guidance:

> Regardless of intent or how or from whom the information was received, suspected, or known, falsification or alteration of records required under parts 210, 211, and 212 must be fully investigated under the cGMP quality system to determine the effect of the event on patient safety, product quality, and data reliability; to determine the root cause; and to ensure the necessary corrective actions are taken (see § 211.22(a), 211.125(c), 211.192, 211.198, 211.204, and 212.100).

The investigation must ensure copies of all data are secured in a timely manner to permit a thorough review of the event and all potentially related processes.

The people involved must be interviewed to better understand the nature of the failure and how it occurred and what might have been done to prevent and detect the issue sooner. This must include discussions with the people involved in data integrity issues, as well as supervisory personnel, quality assurance, and management staff.

The investigation must not be limited to the specific issue identified but must also consider potential impact on previous decisions based upon the data and systems now found to be unreliable. In addition, it is vital that the deeper, underlying root cause(s) of the issue be considered, including potential management pressures and incentives (for example, lack of adequate resources).

Corrective and preventive actions taken must address not only the identified issue, but also previous decisions and data sets that are impacted, as well as deeper, underlying root causes, including the need for realignment of management expectations and allocation of additional resources to prevent risks from recurring in the future.

Regulatory authorities consider it a positive when companies establish internal hotlines to report this type of issue. However, still, many regulated companies are very reluctant to internally investigate data integrity problems, and for those cases, the U.S. FDA established a reporting e-mail. Using the FDA's words, "FDA invites individuals to report suspected data integrity issues that may affect the safety, identity, strength, quality, or purity of drug products at DrugInfo@fda.hhs.gov. 'cGMP data integrity' must be included in the subject line of the e-mail."

12.2 RESPONDING TO SIGNIFICANT DATA INTEGRITY ISSUES

Companies must give primary consideration to solving the immediate issues identified and assessing the risks associated with the data integrity issues. The response by the company must outline the actions taken.

Responses must include a *comprehensive investigation* into the extent of the inaccuracies in data records and reporting, including:

- A detailed investigation protocol and methodology; a summary of all laboratories, manufacturing operations, and systems to be covered by the assessment; and a justification for any part of the operation the company proposes to exclude.

- Hiring a qualified third-party consultant with specific expertise in the areas where potential breaches were identified may be necessary.

- Interviews of current and former employees to identify the nature, scope, and root cause of data inaccuracies. These interviews may be conducted by a qualified third party.

- An assessment of the extent of data integrity deficiencies at the facility. Identify omissions, alterations, deletions, record destruction, noncontemporaneous record completion, and other deficiencies.

- Determination of the scope, extent, and time frame for the incident, with justification for the time boundaries applied.

- Data, products, processes, and specific batches implicated in any investigation.

- A description of all parts of the operations in which data integrity lapses occurred. Additional consideration must be given to global corrective actions for multinational companies or those that operate across multiple sites.

- A comprehensive, retrospective evaluation of the nature of the testing and manufacturing data integrity deficiencies, and the potential root cause(s).

- Evidence of removal at all levels of individuals responsible for problems from cGMP positions.

- A risk assessment of the potential effects of the observed failures on the quality of the medical product involved. The assessment must include analyses of the risks to patients caused by the release of medical products affected by a lapse of data integrity, risks posed by ongoing operations, and any impact on the veracity of data submitted to regulatory agencies, including data related to product registration dossiers. If the risk assessment determines that there was impact on a product already on the market, then a communication to regulatory authorities is required (see Chapter 12.3).

Global corrective and preventive actions taken to address the data integrity vulnerabilities and time frame for implementation, including:

- Interim measures describing the actions to protect patients and to ensure the quality of the medicinal products, such as notifying customers, recalling the product, conducting additional testing, adding lots to the stability program to assure stability (if applicable), the product's application actions, and enhanced complaint monitoring

- Long-term measures describing any remediation efforts and enhancements to procedures, processes, methods, controls, systems, management oversight, and human resources (for example, training, staffing improvements) designed to ensure the integrity of data

Data integrity issues must always be disclosed to regulatory authorities, either immediately or during the next routine surveillance inspection (see Section 12.3). In either case, it's necessary to verify the effectiveness of actions taken to address those data integrity issues and to be able to demonstrate improvement. Some indicators of improvement are:

- Evidence of a thorough and open evaluation of the identified issue and timely and global implementation of effective corrective and preventative actions.

- Evidence of open communication of issues with clients and regulators. Transparent communication must be maintained throughout the investigation and remediation stages. Regulators must be aware that further data integrity failures may be reported as a result of the detailed investigation. Any additional reaction to these notifications must be proportionate to public health risks, to encourage continued reporting.

- Evidence of communication of data integrity expectations across the company, incorporating processes for open reporting of potential issues and opportunities for improvement without repercussions.

- The company must ensure that an appropriate evaluation of the vulnerability of any electronic systems to data manipulation takes place to ensure that follow-up actions have fully resolved all the violations (third-party expertise may be required).

- Implementation of data integrity policies and procedures in line with the principles of this book.

- Implementation of routine data verification practices.

12.3 DISCLOSING DATA INTEGRITY ISSUES TO REGULATORY AGENCIES

Regulatory authorities are much more willing to work with companies that voluntarily disclose and commit to fixing and preventing data integrity problems. If during the investigation of any data integrity issue you discover there are affected product(s) already on the market, then a timely communication must be established to communicate the issue and actions to be taken (for example, recall product) to regulatory authorities.

As part of the commitment to corrective and preventive actions, senior representatives from the company must declare, in writing, that the company commits to full disclosure of issues and their prompt resolution. A management strategy must be submitted to the regulatory authority that includes the details of the global corrective action and preventive action plan. The strategy must include:

- A detailed corrective action plan that describes how the company intends to ensure the reliability and completeness of all the data generated, including analytical data, manufacturing records, and all data submitted to the regulatory authorities.

- A comprehensive description of the root cause(s) of your data integrity lapses, including evidence that the scope and depth of the current action plan is commensurate with the findings of the investigation and risk assessment. This must indicate if individuals responsible for data integrity lapses remain able to influence GMP/GDocP-related or product application data.

On the other hand, if your investigation and associated risk analysis demonstrate that the data integrity issue does not adversely affect any product(s) on the market, then you must prepare all documentation (investigation report, CAPAs, and so on) and present it to regulators during the next routine inspection.

The FDA's expectations regarding how data integrity problems be addressed are summarized in the 2018 guidance as follows:

> FDA encourages you to demonstrate that you have effectively remediated your problems by investigating to determine the problem's scope and root causes, conducting a scientifically sound risk assessment of its potential effects (including impact on data used to support submissions to FDA), and implementing a management strategy, including a global corrective action plan that addresses the root causes. This may include retaining a third-party auditor and

removing individuals responsible for data integrity lapses from positions where they can influence cGMP-related or drug application data at your firm. It also may include improvements in quality oversight, enhanced computer systems, and creation of mechanisms to prevent recurrences and address data integrity breaches (e.g., anonymous reporting system, data governance officials, and guidelines).

These expectations mirror those developed for the Application Integrity Policy.[1]

---

[1] http://www.fda.gov/ICECI/EnforcementActions/ApplicationIntegrityPolicy/ucm 134744.htm. Accessed December 29, 2018.

13

Data Integrity for Outsourced Activities

13.1 GENERAL SUPPLY CHAIN CONSIDERATIONS

Data integrity plays a key role in ensuring the security and integrity of supply chains. Data governance measures established by your company may be significantly weakened by unreliable or falsified data or materials provided by supply chain partners. This principle applies to all outsourced activities, including suppliers of raw materials, contract manufacture, or analytical services, and services such as calibration or pest control activities to mention a few of them.

Initial and periodic requalification of supply chain partners and outsourced activities must include consideration of data integrity risks and appropriate control measures. It is important for a company to understand the data integrity limitations of information obtained from the supply chain (for example, summary records and copies or printouts of those records) and the challenges of remote control and supervision. This will help to focus resources toward data integrity verification and supervision using a quality risk management approach. These limitations will be discussed in Section 13.4.

The supply chain relies upon the use of documentation and data shared between companies. It is often not practical for the client to review all raw data relating to reported results. Emphasis must be placed upon robust supplier and contractor qualification, using the principles of quality risk management. Your control efforts must be commensurate with the criticality of the product or services your received from each supplier.

The increasing outsourcing of GXP work to contracted organizations emphasizes the need to establish and robustly maintain defined roles and responsibilities to ensure complete and accurate data and records throughout these relationships. The responsibilities of the client (contract giver) and the supplier (contract acceptor) must comprehensively address the processes of both parties that must be followed to ensure data integrity. These details must be included in the contract and/or quality agreement relevant to the outsourced work performed or the services provided.

The company that outsources work has the responsibility for the integrity of all results reported, including those furnished by any subcontracting organization or service provider. These responsibilities extend to any providers of relevant computing services. When outsourcing databases and software provision, the contract giver must ensure any subcontractors have been agreed upon and are included in the quality agreement with the contract accepter and are appropriately qualified and trained in good documentation practices/data integrity. Their activities must be monitored on a regular basis at intervals determined through risk assessment. This also applies to cloud-based service providers.

To fulfill this responsibility, in addition to having their own governance systems, outsourcing organizations must verify the adequacy of the governance systems of the supplier, through an audit or other suitable means. This must include the adequacy of the supplier's controls over their own suppliers and a list of significant authorized third parties working for the supplier.

The personnel who evaluate and periodically assess the competence of a contracted organization or service provider must have the appropriate background, qualifications, experience, and training to assess data integrity governance systems and to detect validity issues. The nature and frequency of the evaluation of the supplier and the approach to ongoing monitoring of their work must be based upon a documented assessment of risk. This assessment must include an evaluation of relevant data processes and their risks.

13.2 QUALITY AGREEMENTS WITH YOUR SUPPLIERS

The expected data integrity control strategies must be included in quality agreements and in written contract and technical arrangements, as appropriate and applicable, between the client (contract giver) and the supplier (contract acceptor). These must include provisions for the client to have access to all data held by the contracted organization that are relevant to the contract giver's product or service as well as all relevant quality system records. This must include ensuring access by the contract giver to electronic records, including audit trails, held in the contracted organization's computerized systems as well as any printed reports and other relevant paper or electronic records.

Where data and document retention are contracted to a third party, particular attention must be paid to understanding the ownership and retrieval of data held under this arrangement. The physical location where the data are held, and the impact of any laws applicable to that geographical location, must also be considered. Agreements and contracts must establish mutually agreed consequences if the supplier denies, refuses, or limits the client's access to their records held by the supplier. The agreements and contracts must also contain provisions for actions to be taken in the event of business closure or bankruptcy of the third party to ensure access is maintained and the data can be transferred before the cessation of all business activities.

When outsourcing databases, the contract giver must ensure, if subcontractors are used, in particular cloud-based service providers, they are included in the quality agreement and are appropriately qualified and trained in good documentation practices/data integrity. Their activities must be monitored on a regular basis at intervals determined through risk assessment.

Where "cloud" or "virtual" services are used, attention must be paid to understanding the service provided and the ownership, retrieval, retention, and security of data. The physical location where the data are held, including the impact of any laws applicable to that geographic location, must be considered.

The responsibilities of the client and the supplier must be defined in a technical agreement or contract. This must ensure timely access to data (including metadata and audit trails) to the data owner and national competent authorities upon request. Contracts with providers must define responsibilities for archiving and continued readability of the data throughout the retention period.

Appropriate arrangements must exist for the restoration of the software/system as per its original validated state, including validation and change control information to permit this restoration.

Business continuity arrangements must be included in the contract and tested. The need for an audit of the service provider must be based upon risk.

13.3 STRATEGIES FOR ASSESSING DATA INTEGRITY IN THE SUPPLY CHAIN

Companies must conduct regular risk reviews of supply chains and outsourced activity that evaluate the extent of the data integrity controls required. Information considered during risk reviews may include:

- The outcome of site audits, with focus on data governance measures.

- Review of data submitted in routine reports (for example, comparison of analytical data reported by the supplier against in-house data from analysis of the same material). The objective is to look for discrepant data that may be an indicator of lack of integrity or falsification.

Quality agreements must be in place between manufacturers and suppliers/contract manufacturing organizations (CMOs) with specific provisions for ensuring data integrity across the supply chain. This may be achieved by setting out expectations for data governance, and transparent error/deviation reporting by the supplier to the client. There must also be a requirement to notify the client of any data integrity failures identified at the supplier site.

Audits of suppliers and manufacturers of APIs, critical intermediate material suppliers, and service providers conducted by the manufacturer (or by a third party on their behalf) must include a verification of data integrity measures at the contract organization.

Audits and routine surveillance must include adequate verification of source electronic data and metadata by the quality unit of the client using a quality risk management approach. This may be achieved by measures such as:

- Site audit—Review the supplier's organizational behavior and understanding of data governance, data life cycle, risk, and criticality.

- Material testing versus certificate of analysis (CoA)—Compare the results of analytical testing against the supplier's reported CoA. Examine discrepancies in accuracy, precision, or purity results. This may be performed on a routine basis, periodically, or unannounced, depending on material and supplier risks.

- Remote data review—The client may consider offering the contracted facility/supplier use of their own hardware and software system (deployed over a wide area network) to use in batch manufacture and testing. The client may monitor the quality and integrity of the data generated by the contracted facility personnel in real time. In this situation, there must be segregation of duties to ensure that client monitoring of data does not give provision for amendment of data generated by the supplier.

- Quality monitoring—Quality and performance monitoring may indicate incentive for data falsification (for example, raw materials that marginally comply with specification on a frequent basis).

Clients may work with the supplier to ensure all client-confidential information is encoded to de-identify clients. This would facilitate review of source electronic data and metadata at the contract giver's site, without breaking confidentiality obligations to other clients. By reviewing a larger data set, this enables a more robust assessment of the contract giver's data governance measures. It also permits a search for indicators of data integrity failure, such as repeated data sets or data that does not demonstrate the expected variability.

Care must be taken to ensure the authenticity and accuracy of supplied documentation (refer to Section 13.4). The difference in data integrity and traceability risks between "true copy" and "summary report" data must be considered when making contractor and supply chain qualification decisions.

13.4 LIMITATIONS OF REMOTE REVIEW OF SUMMARY REPORTS

The remote review of data within summary reports is a common necessity; however, the limitations of remote data review must be fully understood to enable adequate control of data integrity.

Summary reports of data are often supplied between physically remote manufacturing sites and other interested parties. However, it must be acknowledged that summary reports are essentially limited in their nature, in that critical supporting data and metadata are often not included and thus original data cannot be reviewed.

It is therefore essential that summary reports are viewed as but one element of the process for the transfer of data and that interested parties and regulators do not place sole reliance on summary report data.

Prior to acceptance of summary data, an evaluation of the supplier's quality system and compliance with data integrity principles must be established through onsite audit when considered important in the context of quality risk management. The audit must ensure the veracity of data generated by the company and include a review of the mechanisms used to generate and distribute summary data and reports.

13.5 JEOPARDIZING YOUR SUPPLY CHAIN

What is expected of a company in the event that one of its approved suppliers (for example, active substance manufacturer, finished product manufacturer, or quality control laboratory) is issued with a warning letter/statement of noncompliance concerning data integrity from a regulatory authority?

First of all, the company must evaluate the risk to its products that are manufactured/released using the principles of quality risk management. Risk assessments must be made available to regulators, on request.

Depending on the outcome of the risk assessment, appropriate action must be taken that may entail delisting the contractor from the approved contractor list. In the event that abnormal disruption in supply may result from a contractor compliance situation, relevant regulatory authorities must be consulted in this regard.

Where does a company's responsibility begin and end in relation to data integrity aspects of the supply chain for medicinal products? All parties in the supply chain play an important part in overall data integrity and assurance of product quality. Data governance systems must be implemented from the manufacture of starting materials right through to the delivery of medicinal products to persons authorized or entitled to supply medicinal products to the public.

Relative responsibilities and boundaries must be documented in the contracts between the relevant parties. Final responsibility of ensuring compliance throughout the supply chain rests with the batch-certifying/approval process.

In summary, data integrity requirements must be incorporated into the company's contractor/vendor qualification/assurance program and associated procedures. In addition to having their own data governance systems, companies outsourcing activities must verify the adequacy of comparable systems at the supplier. The supplier must apply equivalent levels of control to those applied by the client.

Formal assessment of the supplier's competency and compliance in this regard must be conducted in the first instance *prior* to the approval of a supplier, and thereafter verified on a periodic basis at an appropriate frequency based on risk.

How can a recipient (contract giver) build confidence in the validity of documents such as a CoA provided by a supplier (contract acceptor)? The recipient must have knowledge of the systems and procedures implemented at the supplier for the generation of the CoA. Arrangements must be in place to ensure significant changes to systems are notified, and the effectiveness of these arrangements must be subjected to periodic review.

Data related to activities that are outsourced are routinely provided as summary data in a report format (for example, a CoA). These summary documents are reviewed on a routine basis by the contract acceptor, and therefore the review of data integrity at the contract acceptor site on a regular periodic basis (for example, during an onsite audit) takes on even greater significance in order to build and maintain confidence in the summary data provided.

14

Maintaining Integrity of Electronic Data

The use of computerized systems andelectronic data were an early concern for the FDA. In 1976, the agency published an inspection technical guide (ITG) titled "The Computer in FDA Regulated Industries," intended to aid its investigators in understanding computerized operations. The approach was a simplified explanation of the basic principles of the computer with later ITG issues, covering such areas as programming and details of computer operation and specific applications. Reference to this and the other reference documents mentioned below are included in Section 14.11.

In February 1983, the FDA published a guide to inspection of "Computerized Systems in Drug Establishments," discussing some potential problem areas in application of computer systems. The guide also provides inspectional guidance and includes a glossary of terms the investigator should be aware of prior to performing the inspection.

The 21 CFR Part 11, which is the part of Title 21 of the Code of Federal Regulations that establishes the FDA regulations on electronic records and electronic signatures (ERES) was published in 1997. Part 11, as it is commonly called, defines the criteria under which electronic records and electronic signatures are considered trustworthy, reliable, and equivalent to paper records (Title 21 CFR Part 11 Section 11.1 [a]).

Part 11 applies to drug manufacturers, medical device manufacturers, biotech companies, biologics developers, CROs, and other FDA-regulated industries, including food. It requires that they implement controls, including audits, system validations, audit trails, electronic signatures, and documentation, for software and systems involved in processing the electronic data that FDA predicate rules require them to maintain. A predicate rule is any requirement set forth in the federal Food, Drug, and Cosmetic Act, the Public Health Service Act, or any FDA regulation other than Part 11. The rule also applies to submissions made to the FDA in electronic format (for example, an NDA or ANDA), but not to paper submissions by electronic methods (for example, a document sent by fax).

In 2003, the FDA published its guidance for industry: *Part 11, Electronic Records: Electronic Signatures—Scope and Application*. This document was intended to clarify how Part 11 should be implemented and would be enforced. But, as with all FDA guidance documents, it was not intended to convey the full force of law—rather, it expressed the FDA's "current thinking" on Part 11 compliance. Many within the industry, while pleased with the more limited scope defined in the guidance, complained that, in some areas, the 2003 guidance contradicted requirements in the 1997 final rule.

In May 2007, the FDA issued the final version of its guidance on computerized systems in clinical investigations titled "Guidance for Industry Computerized Systems Used in Clinical Investigations." This guidance supersedes the guidance of the same name dated April 1999 and supplements the guidance for industry on *Part 11, Electronic Records; Electronic Signatures—Scope and Application* and the agency's international harmonization efforts when applying these guidance documents to source data generated at clinical study sites.

Regarding the more specific topic of software validation, in 2002, the FDA published a final guidance for industry and FDA staff titled "General Principles of Software Validation." This guidance outlines general validation principles that the agency considers to be applicable to the validation of medical device software or the validation of software used to design, develop, or manufacture medical devices. However, in practice, this guidance is being used to cover the validation of software used across all types of FDA-regulated industries.

This guidance recommends an integration of software life cycle management and risk management activities. Based on the intended use and the safety risk associated with the software to be developed, the software developer should determine the specific approach, the combination of techniques to be used, and the level of effort to be applied. While this guidance does not recommend any specific life cycle model or any specific technique or method, it does recommend that software validation and verification activities be conducted throughout the entire software life cycle. Where the software is developed by someone other than the regulated company (for example, an off-the-shelf software), the software developer may not be directly responsible for compliance with FDA regulations. In that case, the regulated company must assess the adequacy of the off-the-shelf software developer's activities and determine what additional efforts are needed to establish that the software is validated for the regulated manufacturer's intended use.

In the case of PIC/S and the EU, Annex 11 "Computerised Systems" laid out the principles applicable to all forms of computerized systems used as part of GMP-regulated activities. A computerized system is defined as a set of software and hardware components that together fulfill certain functionalities. As part of its principles, this annex established that software applications should be validated, and the IT infrastructure should be qualified. It also establishes that where a computerized system replaces a manual operation, there should be no resultant decrease in product quality, process control, or quality assurance. There should be no increase in the overall risk of the process.

14.1 COMPUTERIZED SYSTEM TRANSACTIONS

Computerized systems must be designed in a way that ensures compliance with the principles of data integrity. The system design must make provisions such that original data cannot be deleted and for the retention of audit trails reflecting changes made to original data.

A computerized system transaction is a single operation or sequence of operations performed as a single logical "unit of work." The operation(s) that makes a transaction may not be saved as a permanent record on durable storage until the user commits the transaction through a deliberate act (for example, pressing a save button), or until the system forces the saving of data.

The metadata (for example, username, date, and time) are not captured in the system audit trail until the user saves the transaction to durable storage. In computerized systems, an electronic signature may be required for the record to be saved and become permanent.

A critical step is a parameter that must be within an appropriate value (limit, range, or distribution) to ensure the safety of the subject or quality of the product or data. Computer systems must be designed to ensure the execution of critical steps is recorded contemporaneously. Where transactional systems are used, the combination of multiple unit operations into a combined single transaction must be avoided, and the time intervals before saving data must be minimized. Systems must be designed to require saving data to permanent memory before prompting users to make changes.

The company must define during the development of the system (for example, via the user requirements specification) what critical steps are appropriate based on the functionality of the system and the level of risk associated. Critical steps must be documented with process controls that consider system design (prevention), together with monitoring and review processes. Oversight of activities must alert to failures that are not addressed by the process design.

A large variety of computerized systems are used by companies to assist in a significant number of operational activities. These range from the simple standalone to large integrated and complex systems, many of which have an impact on the quality of products manufactured. It is the responsibility of each regulated company to fully evaluate and control all computerized systems and manage them in accordance with GMP and GDocP requirements.

Companies must be fully aware of the nature and extent of computerized systems utilized, and assessments must be in place that describe each system, its intended use and function, and any data integrity risks or vulnerabilities that may be susceptible to manipulation. Particular emphasis must be placed on determining the criticality of computerized systems and any associated data in regard to product quality.

The processes for the design, evaluation, and selection of computerized systems must include appropriate consideration of the data management and integrity aspects of the system. Regulated users must ensure new systems include appropriate controls to ensure effective data management. Legacy systems are expected to meet the same basic requirements; however, full compliance may necessitate the use of additional controls, such as supporting administrative procedures or supplementary security hardware/software.

All computerized systems with potential for impact on product quality must be effectively managed under a mature quality management system that is designed to ensure systems are protected from acts of accidental or deliberate manipulation, modification, or any other activity that may impact data integrity.

When determining data vulnerability and risk, it is important that the computerized system is considered in the context of its use within the business process. For example, data integrity of an analytical method with a computerized interface is affected by sample preparation, entry of sample weights into the computerized system, use of the computerized system to generate data, and processing/recording of the final result using that data.

When does electronic data become a cGMP record? When generated to satisfy a cGMP requirement, all data become a cGMP record. You must document, or save, the data at the time of performance to create a record in compliance with cGMP requirements. Regulatory authorities expect processes to be designed so quality data required to be created and maintained cannot be modified without a record of the modification.

As an example, the FDA's 2018 Guidance establishes that:

> For example, chromatographic data should be saved to durable media upon completion of each step or injection (e.g., peak integration or processing steps; finished, incomplete, or aborted injections) instead of at the end of an injection set, and changes to the chromatographic data or injection sequence should be documented in an audit trail. Aborted or incomplete injections should be captured in audit trails and should be investigated and justified.

It is worth noting that the 2016 draft version of the same FDA guide pointed to the same situation, only indicating:

> For example, chromatograms should be sent to long-term storage (archiving or a permanent record) upon run completion instead of at the end of a day's runs.

This change from the draft version to the final format clearly demonstrates how data integrity expectation/requirements are continuously evolving and become more stringent every day.

It is not acceptable to record data on pieces of paper that will be discarded after the data are transcribed to a permanent laboratory notebook. Similarly, it is not acceptable to store data electronically in temporary memory, in a manner that allows for manipulation, before creating a permanent record. Electronic data that are automatically saved into temporary memory do not meet cGMP documentation or retention requirements.

You may employ a combination of technical and procedural controls to meet cGMP documentation practices for electronic systems. For example, a computer system, such as a LIMS or an Electronic Batch Record (EBR) system, can be designed to automatically save after each separate entry. This would be similar to recording each entry contemporaneously on a paper batch record to satisfy cGMP requirements. The computer system configuration must be combined with a procedure requiring data be entered immediately when generated.

14.2 QUALIFICATION AND VALIDATION OF COMPUTERIZED SYSTEMS

The qualification and validation of computerized systems must be performed in accordance with the relevant GMP/GDocP guidelines. Validation alone does not necessarily guarantee that records generated are adequately protected. Thus, validation must be supplemented by appropriate administrative and physical controls, as well as training. Below are specific expectations for ensuring good data governance practices for computerized systems.

Validation documentation

- Regulated users must have an inventory of all computerized systems in use. This list must include reference to:
  - The name, location, and primary function of each computerized system

- Assessments of the function and criticality of the system and associated data (for example, direct GMP/GDocP impact, indirect impact, none)

- The current validation status of each system and reference to existing validation documents

- Risk assessments must be in place for each system, specifically assessing the necessary controls to ensure data integrity. The level and extent of validation for data integrity must be determined based on the criticality of the system and process as well as potential risk to product quality (for example, processes or systems that generate or control batch release data would generally require greater control than those systems managing less critical data or processes).

- Consideration must also be given to those systems with higher potential for disaster or malfunction or situations in which the system becomes inoperative.

- Assessments must also review the vulnerability of the system to inadvertent or unauthorized changes to critical configuration settings or manipulation of data. All controls must be documented, and their effectiveness verified.

- A validation summary report for each computerized system must be in place and include at least the following items:

  - Critical system configuration details and controls for restricting access to configuration and any changes (change control)

  - A list of currently approved users, specifying the user's name and surname, and any specific usernames

  - Identity and permitted activities (privileges) for each user of the system

  - Identity and role of the systems administrator

  - Frequency of review of audit trails and system logs

  - Procedures establishing detailed instructions related to:

    o How a new system user is created

    o The process for the modification (change of privileges) for an existing user

    o The process of deleting users

- ○ Arrangements for backup and frequency
- ○ A description of the recovery process in case of an incident
- ○ Process and responsibilities for data archiving
- ○ Approved locations for data storage
- It must be clearly stated that the original data are retained with relevant metadata in a form that permits the reconstruction of the manufacturing process or the analytical activity.
- Companies must have a validation master plan in place that includes specific policies and validation requirements for computerized systems and the integrity of such systems and associated data.
- The extent of validation for computerized systems must be determined based on risk.
- Before a system is put into routine use, it must be challenged with defined tests for conformance with the acceptance criteria.
- It would be normally expected that a prospective validation for computerized systems is conducted; however, for systems already installed, it may be acceptable to perform retrospective validation based on an assessment of all historical records for the existing computerized system.
- In case of a retrospective qualification, a documented evaluation of system history (for example, error logs, changes made, evaluation of user manuals, and SOPs) would be expected to have taken place.
- IT validation must be designed according to approved procedures, including the following tests:
  - URS (user requirement specifications)
  - FAT (factory acceptance testing)
  - SAT (site acceptance testing)
  - DQ (design qualification)
  - IQ (installation qualification)
  - OQ (operational qualification)
  - PQ (performance qualification)

- Qualification testing includes DQ, IQ, OQ, and PQ. Specific tests must be designed in order to challenge those areas where data integrity is at risk.

- Companies must ensure computerized systems are qualified for their intended use. Companies must therefore not place sole reliance on vendor qualification packages. Validation exercises must include specific tests to ensure data integrity is maintained during operations that reflect normal and intended use.

- The number of tests must be guided by a risk assessment, but the critical functionalities must be at least identified and tested. For example, for certain PLCs and systems based on basic algorithms or logic sets, the functional testing may provide adequate assurance of reliability of the computerized system. For critical and/or more complex systems, detailed verification testing is required during IQ, OQ, and PQ stages.

Periodic evaluation

- Computerized systems must be evaluated periodically to confirm they maintain the validated status and are GMP compliant. The evaluation must include deviations, changes, upgrade history, performance, and maintenance.

- The frequency of the reevaluation must be based on a risk assessment depending on the criticality of the computerized systems. The assessment performed must be documented.

Data transfer between systems

- Interfaces must be assessed and addressed during validation to ensure the correct and complete transfer of data. Interfaces must include appropriate built-in checks for the correct and secure entry and processing of data to minimize data integrity risks. Verification methods may include the use of secure transfer, encryption, check sums, and so on.

- Where system software is installed or updated, the user must ensure archived data can be read by the new software. Where necessary this may require conversion of existing archived data to the new format.

• Where conversion to the new data format of the new software is not possible, the old software must be maintained and installed in one computer and also available as a hard copy (for example, an installation CD) in order to have the opportunity to read the archived data if necessary (for example, in case of an investigation).

14.3 SYSTEM SECURITY FOR COMPUTERIZED SYSTEMS

• User access controls, both physical and electronic, must be configured and enforced to prohibit unauthorized access to, changes to, and deletion of data. For example:

  – Individual login IDs and passwords must be set up and assigned for all staff needing to access and utilize the specific electronic system. Shared login credentials do not allow for traceability to the individual who performed the activity. For this reason, shared passwords must be prohibited.

  – Systems in which a new password cannot be changed by the user, but can only be created by the systems administrator, are incompatible with data integrity, as the confidentiality of passwords cannot be maintained.

  – Input of data and changes to computerized records must be made only by authorized personnel. Companies must maintain a list of authorized individuals and their access privileges for each electronic system in use.

  – Administrator access to computer systems used to run applications must be controlled. General users must not have access to critical aspects of the software (for example, system clocks, file deletion functions, and so on).

  – Systems administrators should normally be independent from users performing the task and have no involvement or interest in the outcome of the data generated or available in the electronic system. For example, quality control (QC) supervisors and managers must not be assigned as the systems administrators for electronic systems in their laboratories (for example, HPLC, gas chromatography (GC), or UV/Vis). Typically, individuals outside of the quality and production organizations (for example, IT administrators) must serve as the systems administrators and have enhanced permission levels.

- For smaller organizations, it may be permissible for a nominated person to hold access as the systems administrator. In these cases, the administrator access must not be used for performing routine operations, and the user must hold a second and restricted access for performing routine operations.

- Any request for new users or new privileges of users must be forwarded to the IT administrator in a traceable way in accordance with a standard procedure.

• Computerized systems must be protected from accidental changes or deliberate manipulation. Companies must assess systems and their design to prevent unauthorized changes to validated settings that may ultimately affect data integrity. Consideration must be given to:

- The physical security of computerized system hardware:

  ○ Location of and access to servers

  ○ Restricting access to PLC nodules (for example, by locking access panels)

- Vulnerability of networked systems from local and external attack

- Remote network updates (for example, automated updating of networked systems by the vendor)

• Firewall rules must be subject to periodic reviews against specifications to ensure they are set as restrictive as necessary, allowing only permitted traffic. The reviews must be documented.

• Electronic signatures used in the place of handwritten signatures must have appropriate controls to ensure their authenticity and traceability to the specific person who electronically signed the record(s). Electronic signatures must be permanently linked to their respective record, and they must automatically log the date and time when the signature was applied.

• The use of advanced forms of electronic signatures is becoming more common (for example, the use of biometrics) and should be encouraged. Section 3.1 includes a discussion on this topic, including the inappropriate use of stored digital images of a person's handwritten signature.

14.4 AUDIT TRAIL AND REVIEW
OF ELECTRONIC DATA

In the case of data generated from an electronic system, electronic data are the original record that must be reviewed and evaluated prior to making product release decisions and other decisions relating to GMP-related activities (for example, approval of stability results, analytical method validation, and so on). If the review is based solely on printouts, there is potential for records to be excluded from the review process, which may contain uninvestigated out-of-specification data or other data anomalies. The review of the raw electronic data must mitigate risk and enable detection of data deletion, amendment, duplication, reusing, and fabrication, which are common data integrity failures.

The regulated user must perform a risk assessment to identify all the GMP/GDocP-relevant electronic data generated by the computerized systems. Once identified, these critical data must be audited by the regulated user and verified to determine that operations were performed correctly and whether any change (modification, deletion, or overwriting) has been made to original information in electronic records. All changes must be duly authorized.

A procedure must describe the process by which data are checked by a second operator. The procedure must outline the critical raw data to be reviewed, the review of data summaries, and the review of any associated logbooks and hard-copy records and must describe how the review is performed, recorded, and authorized.

An example of an inspection observation mentioned in the EMA Q&A document cites:

> Raw data for HPLC/GC runs which had been invalidated was stored separately to the QC raw data packages and had not been included in the review process. In the above situation, the procedure for review of chromatographic data packages did not require a review of the electronic raw data or a review of relevant audit trails associated with the analyses. This lead to the exclusion of records from the review process and to lack of visibility of changes made during the processing and reporting of the data. The company was unable to provide any explanation for the data which had been invalidated.

The audit trail is a form of metadata containing information associated with actions that relate to the creation, modification, or deletion of GXP records. An audit trail provides for secure recording of life cycle details such as creation, additions, deletions, or alterations of information in a record, either paper or electronic, without obscuring or overwriting the original record. An audit trail facilitates the reconstruction of the history of such events relating to the record regardless of its medium, including the "who," "what," "when," and "why" of the action.

Where computerized systems are used to capture, process, report, store, or archive raw data electronically, system design must always provide for the retention of audit trails to show all changes to, or deletion of, data while retaining previous and original data. It must be possible to associate all data and changes to data with the persons making those changes, and changes must be dated and timestamped (time and time zone where applicable). The reason for any change must also be recorded. The items included in the audit trail must be those of relevance to permit reconstruction of the process or activity.

Audit trail function (identified by risk assessment as required) must be switched on. Users must not be able to amend or switch off the audit trail function. When a systems administrator amends or switches off the audit trail, a record of that action must be retained.

The relevance of data retained in audit trails must be considered by the organization to permit robust data review/verification. It is not necessary for audit trail review to include every system activity (for example, user login/logout, every keystroke, and so on).

Where relevant audit trail functionality does not exist (such as within legacy systems), an alternative control may be achieved by, for example, defining the process in an SOP and using logbooks. Alternative controls must be proven to be effective. Where add-on software or a compliant system does not currently exist, continued use of the legacy system may be justified by documented evidence that a compliant solution is being sought and that mitigation measures temporarily support the continued use. It is expected that GMP facilities with industrial automation and control equipment/systems such as programmable logic controllers must be able to demonstrate working toward system upgrades with individual login and audit trails.

Routine data review must include a documented audit trail review where this is determined by a risk assessment. When designing a system for review of audit trails, this may be limited to those with GXP relevance. Audit trails may be reviewed as a list of relevant data, or by an "exception reporting" process. An exception report is a validated search tool that identifies and documents predetermined "abnormal" data or actions that require further attention or investigation by the data reviewer. Reviewers must have sufficient knowledge and system access to review relevant audit trails, raw data, and metadata as required by data governance best practices.

Where systems do not meet the audit trail and individual user account expectations, demonstrated progress must be available to address these shortcomings. This must either be through add-on software that provides these additional functions or by an upgrade to a compliant system. Where remediation has not been identified or subsequently implemented in a timely manner, a deficiency should be cited during self-inspection or regulatory inspections.

How often must audit trails be reviewed? Audit trails that capture changes to critical data must be reviewed with each record and before final approval of the record. Audit trails subject to regular review must include, but are not limited to, the following: the change history of finished product test results, changes to sample run sequences, changes to sample identification, and changes to critical process parameters. Routine, scheduled audit trail review must be based on the complexity of the system and its intended use.

Who must review audit trails? Audit trails are considered part of the associated records. Personnel responsible for record review under cGMP must review the audit trails that capture changes to critical data associated with the record as they review the rest of the record. For example, in the case of the U.S. FDA, all production and control records, which includes audit trails, must be reviewed and approved by the quality unit (§ 211.192). This is similar to the expectation that cross-outs on paper be assessed when reviewing data.

Is a risk-based review of electronic data acceptable? Yes. The principles of quality risk management may be applied during the review of electronic data and review by exception is permitted, when scientifically justified. Exception reporting is used commonly as a tool to focus the review of electronic data such as (but not limited to) electronic batch records. Exception reporting rapidly highlights to the reviewer the exceptions, one of the most critical elements of electronic document review. The level of review of the full electronic record can vary based on the exceptions as well as the level of confidence and experience with a specific process. Appropriate testing and validation must be completed for the automated system and the output exception report to ensure its functionality meets the business and regulatory requirements as per GMP.

Audit trail recommendations

- The review of data-related audit trails must be part of the routine data review within the approval process.

- Audit trails records must be in an intelligible form and have at least the following information:

  – Name of the person who made the change to the data

  – Description of the change

- Time and date of the change

- Justification for the change

- Name of any person authorizing the change

- The frequency, roles, and responsibilities of audit trail reviews must be based on a risk assessment according to the GMP/ GDocP-relevant value of the data recorded in the computerized system. For example, for changes of electronic data that can have a direct impact on the quality of the medicinal products, a review is expected each and every time the data are generated.

- Companies must endeavor to purchase and upgrade software that includes electronic audit trail functionality.

- Where available, audit trail functionalities for electronic-based systems must be configured properly to capture general system events as well as any activities relating to the acquisition, deletion, and overwriting of or changes to data for audit purposes.

- It is acknowledged that some simple systems lack appropriate audit trails; however, alternative arrangements to verify the veracity of data must be implemented (for example, administrative procedures, secondary checks, and controls).

- Audit trails must be verified during validation of the system.

- Audit trail functionalities must always be enabled and locked. For example, an analyst involved in the input of and changes to HPLC data must not have access to enable and disable the audit trail as he/she desires.

- Companies must implement procedures that outline their policy and processes for the review of audit trails in accordance with risk management principles. The procedure must establish in detail the process that the person in charge for the audit trail review must follow.

- Audit trails related to the production of each batch must be independently reviewed with all other records related to the batch and prior to the batch's release to ensure critical data and changes to it are acceptable.

- This review must be performed by the originating department and, where necessary, verified by the quality unit (for example, during self-inspection or investigative activities).

- The audit trail activity must be documented and recorded. The audit trail review records must be maintained together with the other GMP/GDocP-relevant documents.

- The company's quality unit must establish a program and schedule to conduct ongoing reviews of audit trails based upon their criticality and the system's complexity. A sample of the audit trail records must be reviewed during the routine self-inspection.

- Procedures must be in place to address and investigate any audit trail discrepancies, including escalation processes for the notification of senior management and regulatory authorities where necessary.

- Any significant variation from the expected outcome found during the audit trail review must be fully investigated and recorded. A procedure must describe the actions to be taken if a review of audit trails identifies serious issues that can impact the quality of the medicinal products (see Chapter 12).

14.5 DATA CAPTURE/ENTRY

Systems must be designed for the correct capture of data whether acquired through manual or automated means. For manual entry:

- The entry of data must only be made by authorized individuals, and the system must record details of the entry, the individual making the entry, and when the entry was made

- Data must be entered in a specified format that is controlled by the software, and validation activities must verify that invalid data formats are not accepted by the system

- All manual data entries must be verified, either by a second operator or by a validated computerized means

- Changes to entries must be captured in the audit trail and reviewed by an appropriately authorized and independent person

For automated data capture:

- The interface between the originating system, data acquisition, and recording systems must be validated to ensure the accuracy of data

- Data captured by the system must be saved into memory in a format that is not vulnerable to manipulation, loss, or change

- The system software must incorporate validated checks to ensure the completeness of data acquired, as well as any metadata associated with the data

Any necessary changes to data must be authorized and controlled in accordance with approved procedures. For example, manual integrations and reprocessing of laboratory results must be performed in an approved and controlled manner. The company's quality unit must establish measures that ensure changes to data are performed only when necessary and by designated individuals. Any change and modification to original data must be fully documented and must be reviewed and approved by at least one appropriately trained and qualified individual.

14.6 STORAGE, ARCHIVING, AND DISPOSAL OF ELECTRONIC DATA

Storage of data must include the entire original data and metadata, including audit trails, using a secure and validated process. If the data are backed up, or copies of them are made, then the backup and copies must also have the same appropriate levels of controls so as to prohibit unauthorized access to, changes to, and deletion of data or their alteration. For example, a firm that backs up data onto portable hard drives or pen drives must prohibit the ability to delete data from the hard drive. Some additional considerations for the storage and backup of data include:

- True copies of dynamic electronic records can be made, with the expectation that the entire content (all data and metadata) is included and the meaning of the original records is preserved

- Suitable software and hardware must be readily available for accessing data backups or copies

- Routine backup copies must be stored in a remote location (physically separated) in the event of disasters

- Backup data must be readable for the entire duration of the defined regulatory retention period, even if a new version of the software has been updated or substituted for one with better performance

The record retention procedures must include provisions for retaining the metadata. This allows for future queries or investigations to reconstruct the activities that occurred related to a batch.

Data must be archived periodically in accordance with written procedures. Archive copies must be physically secured in a separate and remote location from where backup data are stored. The data must be accessible and readable, and their integrity maintained for all the period of archiving. There must be in place a procedure for restoring archived data in case an investigation is needed. The procedure in place for restoring archived data must be regularly tested.

If a facility is needed for the archiving process, then specific environmental controls and only authorized personnel access must be implemented to ensure the protection of records from deliberate or inadvertent alteration or loss. When a system in the facility must be retired because problems with long-term access to data are envisaged, procedures must assure the continued readability of the data archived. For example, it could be established to transfer the data to another system.

It must be possible to print out a legible and meaningful record of all the data generated by a computerized system (including metadata). If a change is performed to records, it must be possible to also print out the change of the record, indicating when and how the original data were changed. Procedures must be in place that describe the process for the disposal of electronically stored data. These procedures must provide guidance for the assessment of data and allocation of retention periods and describe the manner in which data that are no longer required are disposed of.

14.7 ELECTRONIC SIGNATURES

An electronic signature is a signature in digital form (biometric or nonbiometric) that represents the signatory. This must be equivalent in legal terms to the handwritten signature of the signatory. Firms using electronic signatures must document the controls used to ensure they are able to identify the specific person who signed the records electronically.

The use of electronic signatures must be appropriately controlled with consideration given to:

- How the signature is attributable to an individual

- How the act of "signing" is recorded within the system so it cannot be altered or manipulated without invalidating the signature or status of the entry

- How the record of the signature will be associated with the entry made and how this can be verified

- The security of the electronic signature, so it can only be applied by the "owner" of that signature

Appropriate validation of the signature process associated with a system must be performed to demonstrate suitability and that control over signed records is maintained. Where a paper or PDF copy of an electronically signed document is produced, the metadata associated with an electronic signature must be maintained with the associated document.

The use of electronic signatures must be compliant with the requirements of national and international standards (for example, 21 CFR Part 11 in the case of the U.S. FDA or EudraLex Volume 4 Annex 11 for the EU). The use of advanced electronic signatures must be considered where this method of authentication is required by the risk assessment. Electronic signature or e-signature systems must provide for "signature manifestations"—for example, a display within the viewable record that defines who signed it, their title, and the date (and time, if significant) and the meaning of the signature (such as verified or approved).

An inserted image of a signature or a footnote indicating the document has been electronically signed (where this has been entered by a means other than the validated electronic signature process) is not adequate. Where a document is electronically signed, the metadata associated with the signature must be retained.

14.8 COMPUTERIZED SYSTEM USER ACCESS/SYSTEMS ADMINISTRATOR ROLES

Regulated companies must make full use of access controls to ensure people have access only to functionality that is appropriate for their job role and that actions are attributable to a specific individual. Companies must exercise appropriate controls to ensure changes to computerized records, or input of laboratory data into computerized records, can be made only by authorized personnel. The ability to alter specifications, process parameters, or manufacturing or testing methods must be restricted by technical means where possible (for example, by limiting permissions to change settings or data).

Companies must be able to demonstrate the access levels granted to individual staff members and ensure historical information regarding user access level is available. Where the system does not capture these data, then a record must be maintained outside of the system. Access controls must be applied to both the operating system and application levels. Individual login at operating system level may not be required if appropriate controls are in place to ensure data integrity (for example, no modification, deletion, or creation of data outside the application is possible). To assist in controlling access, it is recommended that regulated companies maintain a list of authorized individuals and their access privileges for each cGMP computer system in use.

For systems generating, amending, or storing GXP data, shared logins or generic user access must not be used. Where the computerized system design supports individual user access, this function must be used. Systems such as material requirements planning (MRP) that are not used in their entirety for GXP purposes but do have elements within them, such as approved suppliers, stock status, location, and transaction histories that are GXP applicable, require appropriate assessment and control.

It is acknowledged that some computerized systems support only a single user login or limited numbers of user logins. Where no suitable alternative computerized system is available, equivalent control may be provided by third-party software or a paper-based method of providing traceability (with version control). The suitability of alternative systems must be justified and documented. Increased data review is likely to be required for hybrid systems because they are vulnerable to nonattributable data changes. Regulatory authorities expect that companies implement systems that comply with current regulatory expectations.

Systems administrator access must be restricted to the minimum number of people possible, taking account of the size and nature of the organization. The systems administrator role, including any rights to alter or delete files and settings, must be assigned to personnel independent from those responsible for the record content. Systems administrator rights permitting activities such as data deletion, database amendment, or system configuration changes must not be assigned to individuals with a direct interest in the data (for example, data generation, data review, or data approval).

A generic systems administrator account must not be allowed. Personnel with systems administrator access privilege must log in with unique credentials that allow actions in the audit trail(s) to be attributed to a specific individual. The intent of this is to prevent giving access to users with potentially a conflict of interest so they can make unauthorized changes that would not be traceable to that person.

If these independent security role assignments are not practical for small operations or facilities with few employees, alternate control strategies must be implemented. For example, in the rare instance that the same person is required to hold the systems administrator role and to be responsible for the content of the records, it is advisable to have a second person review both settings and content. If second-person review is not possible, the U.S. FDA recommends the person recheck settings and his or her own work.

In the case of clinical trials, procedures must require changes in the access right of individuals depending on the status of clinical trial data. For example, once data management processes are complete, the data are "locked" by removing editing access rights.

One of the most common findings during regulatory inspections is the use of shared login accounts for computer systems. Regulated companies must exercise appropriate controls to ensure actions are attributable to a specific individual. When login credentials are shared, a unique individual cannot be identified through the login, and the system would thus not conform to the GMP requirements requiring that GMP date is attributable.

14.9 VALIDATION TO ENSURE GOOD DOCUMENTATION PRACTICES FOR ELECTRONIC DATA

To assure the integrity of electronic data, computerized systems must be validated at a level appropriate for their use and application. Validation must address the necessary controls to ensure the integrity of data, including original electronic data and any printouts or PDF reports from the system. The approach must ensure good documentation practices are implemented and data integrity risks will be properly managed throughout the data life cycle.

Computerized systems must comply with regulatory requirements and associated guidance. These must be validated for their intended purpose, which requires an understanding of the computerized system's function within a process. For this reason, the acceptance of vendor-supplied validation data in isolation of system configuration and users intended use is not satisfactory. In isolation from the intended process or end-user IT infrastructure, vendor testing is likely to be limited to functional verification only and may not fulfill the requirements for performance qualification.

Functional verification demonstrates that the required information is consistently and completely presented. Validation for intended purpose ensures the steps for generating the custom report accurately reflect those described in the data-checking SOP and the report output is consistent with the procedural steps for performing the subsequent review.

Key aspects of validation that help ensure good documentation practices for electronic data include, but are not limited to, the following:

- **User involvement**—Users must be adequately involved in validation activities to define critical data and data life cycle controls that assure data integrity.

Examples of activities to engage users may include: prototyping, user specification of critical data so that risk-based controls can be applied, user involvement in testing to facilitate user acceptance and knowledge of system features, and others.

- **Configuration and design controls**—The validation activities must ensure configuration settings and design controls for good documentation practices are enabled and managed across the computing environment, including both the software application and operating system environments.

Activities include, but are not limited to:

- Documenting configuration specifications for commercial off-the-shelf systems as well as user-developed systems, as applicable

- Restricting security configuration settings for systems administrators to independent personnel, where technically feasible

- Disabling configuration settings that allow overwriting and reprocessing of data without traceability

- Restricting access to time/date stamps

For systems to be used in clinical trials, configuration and design controls must be in place to protect the blinding of the trial (for example, by restricting access to randomization data that may be stored electronically).

- **Data life cycle**—Validation must include assessing risk and developing quality risk mitigation strategies for the data life cycle, including controls to prevent and detect risks throughout the steps of:

- Data generation and capture

- Data transmission

- Data processing

- Data review

- Data reporting, including handling of invalid and atypical data

- Data retention and retrieval

- Data disposal

Activities might include, but are not limited to:

– Determining the risk-based approach to reviewing electronic data and audit trails based upon process understanding and knowledge of potential impact on products and patients

– Writing SOPs defining the review of original electronic records and including meaningful metadata such as audit trails and review of any associated printouts or PDF records

– Documenting the system architecture and data flow, including the flow of electronic data and all associated metadata, from the point of creation through archiving and retrieval

– Ensuring the relationships between data and metadata are maintained intact throughout the data life cycle

• **SOPs and training**—The validation activities must ensure adequate training and procedures are developed prior to release of the system for GXP use. These must address:

– Computerized systems administration

– Computerized systems use

– Review of electronic data and meaningful metadata, such as audit trails, including training that may be required in system features that enable users to efficiently and effectively process data and review electronic data and metadata.

Other validation controls to ensure good data management for both electronic data and associated paper data must be implemented as deemed appropriate for the system type and its intended use.

Regulated industries must validate each workflow on their computer system. A workflow, such as creation of an electronic master production and control record, is an intended use of a computer system to be checked through validation. If you validate the computer system, but you do not validate it for its intended use, you cannot know if your workflow runs correctly. For example, qualifying the manufacturing execution system (MES) platform, a computer system, ensures that it meets specifications; however, it does not demonstrate that a given master production and control record generated by the MES contains the correct calculations. In this example, validating the workflow ensures the intended steps, specifications, and calculations in the master production and control record are accurate. This is similar to reviewing a paper batch record and ensuring all supporting procedures are in place before the batch record is implemented in production.

Regulatory authorities require the implementation of appropriate controls to manage risks associated with each element of the system. Controls that are appropriately designed to validate a system for its intended use address software, hardware, personnel, and documentation.

14.10 BACKUP

Backup and recovery processes must be validated and periodically tested. Each backup must be verified to ensure it has functioned correctly (for example, by confirming the data size transferred matches that of the original record). The backup strategies for the data owners must be documented.

Backups for recovery purposes do not replace the need for the long-term retention of data and metadata in their final form for the purposes of verification of the process or activity. As the U.S. FDA established in the 2016 data integrity draft's guidance:

> FDA uses the term *backup* in § 211.68(b) to refer to a true copy of the original data that is maintained securely throughout the records retention period (for example, § 211.180). The backup file must contain the data (which includes associated metadata) and must be in the original format or in a format compatible with the original format.
>
> This must not be confused with backup copies that may be created during normal computer use and temporarily maintained for disaster recovery (e.g., in case of a computer crash or other interruption). Such temporary backup copies would not satisfy the requirement in § 211.68(b) to maintain a backup file of data.

14.11 SPREADSHEET VALIDATION

One of the most common forms of electronic data is the use of customized spreadsheets for calculations, mainly in the QC laboratories but also in manufacture and other GMP areas. Although there is a requirement to validate a spreadsheet template for its intended use and protect it by restricting permissions to alter the template or delete data, regulated companies often fail to do so, and regulatory observations are not uncommon. Following are a couple of examples of FDA observations.

In July 2013, an FDA warning letter[1] cited:

Additionally, the investigator noticed that the use of the Excel spreadsheets in analytical calculations are neither controlled nor protected from modifications or deletion. The investigator noticed that the calculation for residual solvent uses an Excel spreadsheet that has not been qualified. We are concerned about the data generated by your QC laboratory from nonqualified and uncontrolled Excel spreadsheets.

In October 2015, an FDA warning letter[2] cited:

Two uncontrolled Excel spreadsheets were used to record discrepancies and certain in-process drug quality data. This data was initially missing in the batch manufacturing record. Your firm later entered this data into batch records and backdated them.

Customized spreadsheets must be validated by customizing them to their intended use, including, at a minimum, the following procedural controls:

- Password protection access

- Restrict editing (read only) to avoid the retention of previous data in the template

- Save spreadsheets to a designated location on the server and capture the file location on each spreadsheet

- Change passwords and revalidate the customized spreadsheet periodically

14.12 REFERENCES

Following is a list of valuable references specifically related to the topic of electronic data control and integrity:

EU EudraLex Volume 4: Good Manufacturing Practice Medicinal Products for Human and Veterinary Use (2011). Annex 11: *Computerised Systems.*

---

[1]   https://www.fda.gov/iceci/enforcementactions/warningletters/2013/ucm369409.htm. Accessed December 29, 2018.

[2]   https://www.fda.gov/ICECI/EnforcementActions/WarningLetters/2015/ucm474013.htm. Accessed December 29, 2018.

FDA (1976). *Inspection Technical Guide 23: The Computer in FDA Regulated Industries.*

FDA (1983). *Guide to Inspection of Computerized Systems in Drug Establishments.*

FDA (1997). *21 CFR Part 11, Electronic Records; Electronic Signatures.*

FDA (2002). *Final Guidance for Industry and FDA Staff—General Principles of Software Validation.*

FDA (2003). *Guidance for Industry—Part 11, Electronic Records; Electronic Signatures—Scope and Application.*

FDA (2007). *Guidance for Industry: Computerized Systems Used in Clinical Investigations.*

International Society for Pharmaceutical Engineering (ISPE) (2008). *GAMP 5 Guide: A Risk-Based Approach to Compliant GxP Computerized Systems.* Tampa, FL: ISPE.

International Society for Pharmaceutical Engineering (ISPE) (2017). *Records and Data Integrity Guide.* Tampa, FL: ISPE.

Lopez, Orlando (2017). *Data Integrity in Pharmaceutical and Medical Devices Regulation Operations.* Boca Raton, FL: CRC Press.

Parenteral Drug Association (PDA) (2018). *Technical Report No. 80: Data Integrity Management System for Pharmaceutical Laboratory.* Bethesda, MD: PDA.

Rattan, Anil (2018). "Data Integrity: History, Issues, and Remediation of Issues." *PDA J Pharm Sci Technol* 72 (March/April 2018): 105–116.

Appendix A

Examples of FDA's Enforcement Actions for Data Integrity Problems

For those avid readers, a simple search online will provide the original FDA documents mentioned in the following table.

Selected enforcement actions for data integrity problems

Fiscal year	Company	FDA findings
2000	Schein Pharmaceutical, New Jersey (USA). Sterile finished product manufacturer site.	Warning letter citing lack of or inadequate control over laboratory computer systems including password control and staff authority to change data. "Failure to maintain the integrity and adequacy of the laboratory's computer systems used by the Quality Control Unit in the analysis and processing of test data. For example: a) There was a lack of a secure system to prevent unauthorized entry in restricted data systems. Data edit authorization rights were available to all unauthorized users, not only the system administrator."

Selected enforcement actions for data integrity problems (continued)

Fiscal year	Company	FDA findings
2005	Able Laboratories, New Jersey (USA). Manufacturer of generic drugs.	The 15-page 483 form was among the early 483 forms addressing the broad category of data integrity. Failing laboratory results were identified that were not reported, as well as the failure to review electronic data including audit trail. Resulted in withdrawal of near 50 ANDAs and the firm is no longer in business. In 2007, the vice president in charge of the quality control department and three supervisory chemists pleaded guilty to a conspiracy involving the rampant falsification and manipulation of testing data of its drugs. The four were included in the FDA Debarment List. All four admitted participating in a conspiracy spanning from approximately 1999 through mid-2005. The four outlined their supervisory roles and participation with other chemists, which resulted in flouting, altering, and manipulating testing and reporting requirements that were required to be submitted to the FDA.
2006–2014	Ranbaxy sites. Five located in India and one in New York (USA). These facilities are now owned by Sun Pharmaceutical.	Several warning letters, import alerts, and consent decrees covering six manufacturing sites were issued from 2006 to 2014. See Section 5.1 for details about Ranbaxy issues. In 2009, the FDA invoked its AIP against the Paonta Sahib site in India, due to falsified data and test

Selected enforcement actions for data integrity problems (continued)

Fiscal year	Company	FDA findings
		results in approved and pending drug applications from the site that had been under an FDA Import Alert since September 2008. The AIP is invoked when a company's actions raise significant questions about the integrity of data in drug applications.
		In May 2013, the U.S. Department of Justice announced that Ranbaxy pleaded guilty and agreed to pay $500 million to resolve false claims allegations, cGMP violations, and false statements to the FDA. This is the largest drug safety settlement to date with a generic drug manufacturer, where Ranbaxy USA, a subsidiary of Indian generic pharmaceutical manufacturer Ranbaxy Laboratories Limited, pleaded guilty to felony charges relating to the manufacture and distribution of certain adulterated drugs made at two of Ranbaxy's manufacturingfacilities in India. Ranbaxy also agreed to pay a criminal fine and forfeiture totaling $150 million and to settle civil claims under the False Claims Act and related state laws for $350 million.
		Below are some citations from the warning letter received at the New York's Ohm site in 2009:
		"3. Your firm has not established laboratory control mechanisms and documented the execution of laboratory control functions at the time of performance [21 CFR § 211. l60(a)]. For example,

Selected enforcement actions for data integrity problems (continued)

Fiscal year	Company	FDA findings
		Your QCU did not document the dates at the time samples were allegedly withdrawn from the stability chambers for analysis. The attendance record shows that your stability coordinator was absent from your firm during those dates in which the coordinator recorded the withdrawal of samples from the stability chambers (see examples below).
		Your QCU has not established a record control system that assures the reliability of the laboratory raw data. Your QCU documented raw data (e.g., date of analysis, batch numbers, calculations) in spiral pocket notebooks that lack controls to prevent the deletion and traceability of analytical raw data.
		5. Your firm has not exercised appropriate controls over computer or related systems to assure that changes in control records or other records are instituted only by authorized personnel [21 CFR § 211.68(b)J]. For example, one user account is established for two analysts to access the laboratory instrument's software on the computer system attached to HPLC systems. The user account provides full system administrative rights, including editing of the methods and projects. In addition, data security protocols are not established that describe the user's roles and responsibilities in terms of privileges to access, change, modify, create, and delete projects and data."

Selected enforcement actions for data integrity problems (continued)

Fiscal year	Company	FDA findings
		Still in January 2014, one of the company's API manufacturing sites located in Nagar, Punjab (India), received an 11-page 483 form focused almost entirely on the analytical laboratory operation with numerous instances of lack of controls and data integrity issues. Some of the observations were:
		"Raw materials, intermediates, and finished API analytical results found to be failing specifications or otherwise suspect (OOT) are retested until acceptable results are obtained. These failing, or otherwise suspect results, are not reported."
		"Appropriate controls are not established over computerized systems."
		One of the citations relates to the direct observation by the two FDA inspectors of a QC analyst backdating data in a laboratory notebook.
2006–2017	Wockhardt. Indian manufacturers of APIs and finished pharmaceuticals with sites in India, the United Kingdom, and Illinois (USA).	The Mumbai-based pharmaceutical company Wockhardt had received six warning letters (some covering more than one site) for seven manufacturing sites between 2006 and 2017. Three of the Indian sites have been banned from shipping to the United States.

Selected enforcement actions for data integrity problems (continued)

Fiscal year	Company	FDA findings
		The most recent warning letter issued on February 17, 2017, covers the FDA inspection at the Morton Grove, Illinois, drug manufacturing plant. Among the most significant cGMP violations were data integrity issues where the company failed to exercise appropriate controls over computer or related systems to assure that only authorized personnel institute changes in master production and control records, or other records. For example:
		"Our investigators observed that information technology (IT) staff at your facility share usernames and passwords to access your electronic storage system for (b)(4) data. Your IT staff can delete or change directories and files without identifying individuals making changes. After a previous inspection in which FDA observed similar deficiencies, you committed to eliminate these and other data integrity vulnerabilities."
		This warning letter included the following statement:
		"At this time, seven Wockhardt facilities (including Morton Grove) are considered out of compliance with cGMP. These repeated failures at multiple sites demonstrate your company's inadequate oversight and control over the manufacture of drugs."

Selected enforcement actions for data integrity problems (continued)

Fiscal year	Company	FDA findings
		A few months earlier (December 2016), the FDA sent another warning letter to the company following an eight-day inspection in 2015 of its Ankleshwar, India, manufacturing site that uncovered the destruction of cGMP documents among a list of other major violations. The inspector found "torn and shredded equipment maintenance documents, raw material labels, and change control work orders" in the site's scrap yard awaiting incineration.
		The site has been banned from shipping products to the United States since August 2016. In addition to the burning of sensitive documents, FDA inspectors observed employees working in gowns that put the site's drugs at risk of contamination because of "unraveled stitching extending from hoods, zippers, and pants."
		The agency also said its inspector "found unreported results, including an OOS test result for raw materials. You did not investigate this OOS result or explain why you excluded the failing result from the official record."
		Wockhardt employees also had unofficial notebooks with records of sample preparation for OOS investigations, route-of-synthesis experiments, and scale-up

Selected enforcement actions for data integrity problems (continued)

Fiscal year	Company	FDA findings
		data. "Our investigator found discrepancies between these unofficial notebooks and the official data retained by your quality unit," the FDA cited.
		The company's CP Pharmaceuticals subsidiary in Wrexham, United Kingdom, also received a warning letter in November 2016.
2006–2009	Actavis Totowa. Manufacturing site in Little Falls, New Jersey (USA).	In the August 2016 warning letter, the FDA cited that the company failed to submit complete and/or accurate information on some regulatory-required reports such as the 15-day alert reports. Examples of information that were omitted from the submitted reports include previous conditions of patients, concomitant medication, event recurrence, and, follow-up information obtained from patients' physicians.
		The February 2017 warning letter includes observations such as the following:
		"Our investigators uncovered out-of-specification test results in laboratory raw data that were not documented in laboratory notebooks and found that products were released based on retesting without any justification for discarding the initial out-of-specification test results."

Selected enforcement actions for data integrity problems (continued)

Fiscal year	Company	FDA findings
		"2. Our investigators observed that laboratory notebooks did not include all raw test data generated during testing and that analysts do not always document the preparation and testing of samples in their notebooks at the time they are done. Instances were found where analysts aborted and failed to complete chromatographic testing runs after an out-of-specification test result was obtained. The chromatographic test data reflecting the out-of-specification test results were not recorded in laboratory notebooks. Instead, a new sample preparation was injected within the same chromatographic run without supervisory approval, as required by your firm's SOP QC-59, 'Investigation of Out of Specification (OOS) Results.' Our investigators also uncovered numerous instances." Other significant observations related to the following: • The audit trail for the data acquisition system did not indicate aborted runs or discarded data. • There was also a failure to routinely check the lab system's input/output for accuracy. Discrepancies were found between laboratory notebook data and electronic records. Electronic data files were not checked for accuracy.

Selected enforcement actions for data integrity problems (continued)

Fiscal year	Company	FDA findings
2008	Sandoz Wilson manufacturing site in North Carolina (USA).	In an August 2008 warning letter, the FDA included the following observations related to good documentation practices/data integrity:
		"3. Failure to include in-process and laboratory control results in the batch record as required by 21 CFR § 211.188(b)(5). For example, your firm did not have documentation in the batch record of all Metoprolol Succinate ER Tablets (25 mg and 50 mg) pre-compression sample hardness results, dissolution results, and hardness targets which are determined for each lot. These production and testing steps are part of current firm practice and were instituted to define compression parameters due to variability in the Metoprolol ER pellet lots for the 25 and 50 mg tablets.
		During the inspection, you could not locate any documentation for some of these start-up hardness results, and this information was not included in the batch production records. Your firm failed to document these results for any Metoprolol 25 mg tablet lots manufactured in 2006. As a result, QA did not review pre-compression data when reviewing the batch for release, in order to assure that the appropriate hardness was used throughout the manufacturing process.

Selected enforcement actions for data integrity problems (continued)

Fiscal year	Company	FDA findings
		Documentation for the pre-compression samples for the 25 and 50 mg lots was occasionally maintained by the compression supervisor, who decided what target hardness to provide to operators for use in a given lot. Notably, there was no range specified. This information was also not included in the batch production records. In your April 29, 2008, response to the FDA 483, you committed to amend your master batch records to include all pre-compression data, but you provided no explanation regarding the data that was missing at the time of the inspection.
		6. Failure to establish appropriate controls over computer or related systems to assure changes in master production and control records or other records are instituted only by authorized personnel as required by 21 CFR § 211.68 (b).
		For example, the [redacted] data acquisition system for the [redacted] UV/Vis spectrophotometers allows your analysts to modify, overwrite, and delete original raw data files. The spectrophotometers are used for dissolution testing of finished product, stability samples, and process and method validation studies. All laboratory personnel were given roles as [redacted] Managers, which allowed them to modify, delete, and overwrite results files. This system also does not include an audit trail

Selected enforcement actions for data integrity problems (continued)

Fiscal year	Company	FDA findings
		or any history of revisions that would record any modification or deletion of raw data or files. Your laboratory computer system lacks necessary controls to ensure that data is protected from tampering, and it also lacks audit trail capabilities to detect data that could be potentially compromised."
2011	Bioanalytical Cetero Research, Texas (USA). Clinical testing site.	In an untitled letter sent May 2011, the FDA cited that "FDA investigators have identified significant violations of the bioavailability and bioequivalence requirements of Title 21, Code of Federal Regulations, Part 320. These violations include the widespread falsification of dates and times in laboratory records for subject sample extractions, and the apparent manipulation of equilibration samples to meet predetermined acceptance criteria.
		It is your firm's responsibility to ensure and confirm the reliability of your testing methods and the bioequivalence and bioavailability data collected by your firm and presented as part of any applications submitted to the FDA. The pervasiveness and egregious nature of the violative practices by your firm has led FDA to have significant concerns that the bioequivalence and bioavailability data generated at the Cetero Houston facility from April 1, 2005, to June 15, 2010, including data relied on as part of studies submitted in both New Drug Applications (NDA) and Abbreviated New Drug Applications (ANDA) to FDA, are unreliable."

Selected enforcement actions for data integrity problems (continued)

Fiscal year	Company	FDA findings
		According to the FDA's untitled letter to Cetero, an employee first raised concerns with Cetero's management in June 2007 and April 2009: "[The complainant] was aware that many of the chemists were manipulating and falsifying data associated with the samples being used within various projects."
		The FDA sent a letter to the firms that contracted with Cetero Research for clinical studies requesting specific information to establish validity of the clinical studies information included in their drug applications.
		Dozens of drug companies have done clinical testing work through Cetero. At the time of FDA inspection (mid-2010), there were 122 drug studies in progress in which Cetero had some role.
		In March 2012, Cetero filed for bankruptcy.
2013	Hospira, North Carolina (USA). Sterile finished product site.	A 22-page 483 included several data integrity issues. Among them: "The raw data generated from the semi-automated thickness tester used to measure the thickness of perimeter seals on fabricated 500 mL and 1000 mL bags used as container closure systems for injectable drugs can be overwritten with new data without explanation and the original data is erased from the computer's memory upon being overridden."

Selected enforcement actions for data integrity problems (continued)

Fiscal year	Company	FDA findings
2013	Fresenius Kabi Oncology. API site located in Kalyani, Nadia (India).	A warning letter issued July 2013 cited unacceptable practices in the management of data. Two examples are as follows: "We observed and documented practices during the inspection that kept some samples, data, and results outside of the local systems for assessing quality. This raises serious concerns regarding the integrity and reliability of the data generated at your Kalyani plant." "Unacceptable practices in the management of electronic data were also noted. The management of electronic data permitted unauthorized changes, as digital computer folders and files could be easily altered or deleted." This was the first FDA warning letter mentioning the newly approved FDASIA: "During the inspection, your firm also repeatedly delayed, denied, limited, or refused to provide information to the FDA investigators. Please be reminded that the Food and Drug Administration Safety and Innovation Act (FDASIA) § 707 also deems a product to be adulterated if drugs have been manufactured, processed, packed, or held in an establishment by an owner or operator who has delayed, denied, or limited an inspection."

Selected enforcement actions for data integrity problems (continued)

Fiscal year	Company	FDA findings
2014	Sun Pharmaceutical Industries. API and finished dosage manufacturing site located in Mumbai (India).	The warning letter included, among others, the following citations: "Failure to ensure that laboratory records included complete data derived from all tests necessary to ensure compliance with established specifications and standards. For example, a. Your firm is missing the fundamental raw data and information necessary to document your analyses. For example, these analyses lack the following critical data: • Identification of the samples tested, including name and source, batch number or other distinctive code, and date of the sample • The complete record of all raw data generated during each test, including graphs and electronic files from laboratory instrumentation • Test method used • Sample preparation as prescribed by the method, preparation and testing of standards, reagents, and standard solutions • Records of all calculations performed in connection with the test • Test results

Selected enforcement actions for data integrity problems (continued)

Fiscal year	Company	FDA findings
		• The signature of the person who performed each test and the date(s) the tests were performed, and the date and signature of a second person showing that the original records have been reviewed for accuracy, completeness, and compliance with prescribed acceptance criteria"
		"Your firm frequently performs 'unofficial testing' of samples, disregards the results, and reports results from additional tests."
		"Your Senior QC Officer confirmed that QC laboratory employees had frequently practiced the use of 'trial' injections at your facility. Significantly, in addition to the example above, our inspection found 5301 deleted chromatograms on a computer used to operate two HLPC instruments in your QC laboratory. Many of these files were 'trial' injections of batches."
		"Your firm failed to maintain written production, control, or distribution records specifically associated with a batch of a drug product for at least one year after the expiration date of the batch (21 CFR 211.180(a))."
		"Your firm failed to maintain written production, control, or distribution records specifically associated with a batch of a drug product for at least one year after the expiration date of the batch (21 CFR 211.180(a))."

Selected enforcement actions for data integrity problems (continued)

Fiscal year	Company	FDA findings
2014	Trifarma S.p.A. Italian API manufacturer.	In a warning letter issued July 2014, the FDA cited: "1. Failure to maintain complete data derived from all testing and to ensure compliance with established specifications and standards pertaining to data retention and management. Your firm did not retain complete raw data from testing performed to ensure the quality of your APIs. Specifically, your firm deleted all electronic raw data supporting your high-performance liquid chromatography (HPLC) testing of all API products released to the U.S. market. In addition, your firm failed to retain basic chromatographic information such as injection sequence, instrument method, or integration method for the tests. Your firm's lack of data control causes us to question the reliability of your data. In addition, your laboratory management was unaware of, and therefore did not follow, the written procedure detailing the review of analytical data. Furthermore, your management confirmed that the review of analytical data did not include evaluating the system suitability parameters to ensure proper column performance.

Selected enforcement actions for data integrity problems (continued)

Fiscal year	Company	FDA findings
		2. Failure to prevent unauthorized access or changes to data and to provide adequate controls to prevent omission of data.
		Your firm did not have proper controls in place to prevent the unauthorized manipulation of your laboratory's raw electronic data. Specifically, your laboratory systems did not have access controls to prevent deletion or alteration of raw data. The inspection noted that all laboratory employees were granted full privileges to the computer systems.
		In addition, prior to January 7, 2014, HPLC and GC computer software lacked active audit trail functions to record changes to data, including information on original results, the identity of the person making the change, and the date of the change.
		3. Failure to ensure that employees receive appropriate and documented training on the particular operations that the employee performs.
		Your firm did not document any training of production employees on the production operations they perform. Specifically, operators in Synthesis Plant (b)(4) did not have any documented on-the-job training associated with the production operations they perform. In addition, your management was unaware that they should follow

Selected enforcement actions for data integrity problems (continued)

Fiscal year	Company	FDA findings
		the SOP for the issuance of CoAs, which provides for a review of relevant analytical data. Without documented training, there is a lack of assurance that your employees can reliably execute their API manufacturing responsibilities."
2014–2015	Cadila Pharmaceutical, India. API manufacturer.	In an October 2014 warning letter amended February 2015, the FDA cited: "3. Failure to prevent unauthorized access or changes to data and to provide adequate controls to prevent omission of data. Your firm did not have proper controls in place to prevent the unauthorized manipulation of your electronic raw data. For example, a. The inspection found that the audit trail feature for your GC instruments was not used until October 2013, even though your 2009 GC software validation included a satisfactory evaluation of the audit trail capability. b. There is no assurance that you maintain complete electronic raw data for the (b)(4) GC instruments, the Malvern particle size analyzer, and the ultraviolet (UV) spectrophotometer. Our inspection found that these instruments were connected to standalone computers that stored the data and that the data could be deleted.

Selected enforcement actions for data integrity problems (continued)

Fiscal year	Company	FDA findings
		c. Prior to our inspection, your firm failed to have a backup system for the data generated by one of the (b)(4) Fourier-transform infrared spectrometers, the polarimeter, the UV spectrophotometer, and the Malvern particle size analyzer."
		In a December 2015 warning letter covering two sites, the following observations were identified for one of the sites:
		"2. Your firm failed to exercise sufficient controls over computerized systems to prevent unauthorized access or changes to data.
		a. Your firm failed to adequately control the use of computerized systems in the quality control laboratory. Our inspection team found that the laboratory manager had the ability to delete data from the Karl Fischer Tiamo software. During our limited review of your Karl Fischer data, we found that one file had been deleted. However, because the audit trail function for the Karl Fischer Tiamo software was not activated, and because eight different analysts share a single username and password, you were unable to demonstrate who performed each operation on this instrument system. You do not have a record of the acquisition of all data, nor do you have records of changes to or modifications of such data.

Selected enforcement actions for data integrity problems (continued)

Fiscal year	Company	FDA findings
		3. Your firm failed to ensure that all quality-related activities are recorded at the time they are performed.
		Our inspection found that your firm's employees use 'rough or unofficial notebooks' to document various cGMP activities. During their walkthrough, our investigators found 'unofficial' notebooks in the engineering office at your Zyfine (b)(4) plant, in the quality assurance office at your Zyfine (b)(4) plant, and in the scrap yard shared by (b)(4) plants.
		a. For example, an 'unofficial' notebook found in the engineering office stated, 'Pseudomonas present in (b)(4) water system' on November 26, 2014, and '(b)(4) water system (Activity) investigation' on November 25, 2014. Your firm was unable to provide the investigators with any documentation regarding *Pseudomonas sp.* found in your water system and the related investigation.
		b. Our investigators found several plastic bags filled with paperwork and other scrapped items in the scrap yard. One item was a torn notebook of deficiencies recorded during review of your batch manufacturing records. For example, page 22 included a comment on batch (b)(4) 'not mentioned any deviations of lower yield.' Our review of the batch record (b)(4) found that the yield reported was (b)(4)% (range: (b)(4)%), but the batch record did not indicate a deviation.

Selected enforcement actions for data integrity problems (continued)

Fiscal year	Company	FDA findings
		c. On their December 1, 2014, walkthrough of the Zyfine (b) (4) plant, our investigators reviewed AHU/HVAC filter cleaning records. Duplicate records were in the engineering office. One of your firm's representatives stated that the records were rewritten for clarity. Our review of the original and rewritten records found discrepancies in cleaning dates and cleaning personnel."
2015	Dr. Reddy's Laboratories Limited. API and finished drug manufacturing sites in India.	In a warning letter dated November 2015, the FDA cited, among other significant deviations, the following: "1. Failure to maintain complete data derived from all laboratory tests conducted to ensure compliance with established specifications and standards. Your laboratory records did not contain all raw data generated during each test for API batches manufactured at your firm. The investigator found that batch samples were routinely retested following failing or atypical results until acceptable results were obtained, and that failing or atypical results were not investigated or included in the official laboratory control records. During the inspection, the presence of an uncontrolled 'Custom QC laboratory' (CQC) was discovered by our inspection team. The existence

Selected enforcement actions for data integrity problems (continued)

Fiscal year	Company	FDA findings
		of this laboratory was previously unknown to FDA. Your QC Associate Director acknowledged that the CQC laboratory was involved in cGMP analysis of APIs intended for export to the United States through 2012.
		This discovery was made one day before the end of the inspection, but during FDA's brief evaluation of the high-performance liquid chromatography (HPLC) electronic records generated by the CQC, our investigators found numerous instances of violations.
		2. Failure to prevent unauthorized access or changes to data, and to provide adequate controls to prevent omission of data. During the inspection we found the following examples of uncontrolled access to electronic systems used to generate data in your Product Development Laboratory (PD Lab).
		a. Your HPLC systems are configured so that no passwords are required to log in. Credentials are unverified. Anyone who accesses the system can use software administrator privileges, which means that there is no electronic or procedural control to prevent manipulation of data.
		b. Your HPLC system had no access controls to prevent alteration or deletion of data. Furthermore, your HPLC software lacked an audit trail feature to document all activities

Selected enforcement actions for data integrity problems (continued)

Fiscal year	Company	FDA findings
		related to the chromatographic analysis. Because of this failure, neither your quality unit nor your laboratory staff could demonstrate that HPLC records included complete and unaltered data. They were also unable to verify that there had been no alterations or deletions.
		c. One of your analysts stated that another, unknown individual had logged into the system using the analyst's credentials. This unknown individual performed injections and deletions without the analyst's knowledge."
2016	Chongqing Lummy Pharmaceutical Company, Chongqing (China). API manufacturer.	The company received a warning letter on June 2016 citing two outrageous situations: "1. Failure to prevent unauthorized access or changes to data and failure to provide adequate controls to prevent manipulation and omission of data. During the inspection, FDA's investigator discovered a lack of basic laboratory controls to prevent changes to and deletions from your firm's electronically stored data. Your firm relied on incomplete and falsified records to evaluate the quality of your drugs and to determine whether your drugs conformed with established specifications and standards.

Selected enforcement actions for data integrity problems (continued)

Fiscal year	Company	FDA findings
		Our investigator found that your firm failed to prevent data manipulation on multiple computerized analytical systems. Your firm retested samples without justification and deleted raw analytical data from computerized systems. You are responsible for determining the causes of these deviations, for preventing their recurrence, and for preventing other deviations from cGMP.
		a. Our investigator's review of the audit trail for the residual solvent stability testing indicated that an analyst manipulated your computerized GC to falsify residual solvent stability results for multiple batches of (b)(4) API distributed to the U.S.
		For example, on March 4, 2016, your analyst set the GC personal computer (PC) clock back to make it appear as if testing had been done seven months earlier—on August 3, 2015. The analyst then performed five different injections to produce falsified results for long term stability 25C/65% RH 12 months' time-point residual solvent testing for finished API lot (b)(4). The analyst deleted the first four backdated results and reported only the results of the fifth

Selected enforcement actions for data integrity problems (continued)

Fiscal year	Company	FDA findings
		and final injection as passing in the quality control data package. Your quality unit relied on this incomplete data package to evaluate the quality of this lot of API and determine whether it was within specification. Our investigator observed that long-term stability results for at least five other lots of (b)(4) API were falsified using this technique of setting back the clock on the GC personal computer and then performing multiple injections until favorable results were obtained. Your firm failed to prevent analysts' access to manipulate and delete laboratory data. In addition, your laboratory equipment lacked software controls to assure data integrity.
		2. Failure to document manufacturing operations at the time they are performed. During the inspection, our investigator reviewed 20 executed batch manufacturing records and found that most of them contained similar or identical entries that could not be adequately explained. For example, our investigator examined batch records for (b)(4) different batches of (b)(4) API manufactured between January and February 2015. All (b)(4) batch records indicated that certain process steps or measurements had transpired at exactly the same time for each different batch. When our investigator asked your production supervisor to explain why the timestamps

Selected enforcement actions for data integrity problems (continued)

Fiscal year	Company	FDA findings
		were identical on these records, the production supervisor stated that the full manufacturing process takes (b)(4) to complete, and that all batch records are kept in the production area until (b)(4) lots are completed. The production supervisor stated that the operators most likely did not record the actions at the time they were performed but rather completed batch records in groups."
2017	Prosana Distribuciones S.A. de C.V., Mexico City (Mexico). Drug manufacturer.	At the end of 2017, the firm received a warning letter and placed the firm in Import Alert due to, among other observations, the following: "3. Your firm failed to prepare batch production and control records for each batch of drug product that include complete documentation of the accomplishment of each significant step in the manufacture, processing, packing, or holding of the batch, including a statement of the actual yield, and a statement of a percentage of theoretical yield at appropriate phases of processing. (21 CFR 211.188(b)(7)). During the inspection, your firm's management stated that operators 'made up' yield results in your batch records for processing steps such as weighing, (b)(4), and filling, as well as for label reconciliation. Management informed our investigator that operators falsified batch records because there were no established calculations for determining yields."

Selected enforcement actions for data integrity problems (continued)

Fiscal year	Company	FDA findings
2018	Alkem Laboratories, Daman (India). Drug manufacturer.	A 16-page 483 form issued March 27, 2018, included, among others, the following observations: "Specifically, your firm failed to assure the accuracy and reliability for data recorded, which are derived or entered using nonvalidated and unprotected Excel spreadsheets that are not managed and controlled to ensure unauthorized changes do not occur per your firm's written procedures. On March 19, 2018, we observed your QC Managers use an Excel spreadsheet to track quality functions, such as stability samples. This document is not maintained through document control and there is no protection from data manipulation, overwriting, erasing of data, or audit trails." "Established laboratory control mechanisms are not documented at the time of performance. Specifically, During our inspection of the QC laboratory on March 19, 2018, we observed your QC Analyst entering data electronically into an Excel spreadsheet, in the absence of raw data. This same data was also entered into the 9M Stability Study Logbook."

Appendix B

An Example of Data Integrity Training Certification

The following is an example of a comprehensive data integrity training certification our company recently developed:

Training Title: Data Integrity Certification (CERT-015)

Overview: Data integrity is a global mandatory requirement for the regulated healthcare industry. Developing a medical product and bringing it to market involves different players and activities. A fundamental step is linked to the robustness and accuracy of the data submitted by manufacturers to regulatory authorities. That data must be comprehensive, complete, accurate, and true to ensure the quality of studies supporting applications for medical products to be placed on the market. Complete, consistent, and accurate data should be ALCOA. It also must comply with GMPs, GCPs, and GLPs.

Data integrity is a basic element of good documentation practices, one of the most fundamental pillars of any quality management system, including current good manufacturing practices.

Target Group for the Training: Data integrity three-day certification will benefit managers and staff from manufacturing, QC/QA, and analytical development laboratories of pharmaceutical, medical device, and API manufacturers. Auditors responsible for performing self-inspections or external audits will also benefit from this certification.

Learning Objectives: Upon completing this certification, participants will be able to:

 – Understand what data integrity is

- Identify typical documentation and data integrity failures and how to avoid them

- Apply data integrity compliance plans and accountability structures

- Apply techniques to identify and investigate aberrant data patterns

Materials: Each participant will receive:

- MS PowerPoint presentations

- Guidelines, warning letters, and supplemental information

A very comprehensive training effectiveness evaluation system will be conducted using the Kirkpatrick model. A pretest prior to the beginning of the training, plus a post-test at the end of the training, will be completed. A minimum grade of 70% in the post-test is required to pass the certification.

Training Duration: 21 contact hours

Title: Data integrity certification (day 1)

Lunch: 12:00–13:00

Coffee Break: 15 minutes each during morning and afternoon session. Time schedules are rough estimates and may vary consequently.

Agenda	
8:30–9:30	**Opening Remarks and Pretest**
9:30–10:15	**Introduction** • Learn the importance of data integrity • Define data integrity concepts, regulatory actions, and requirements
10:15–10:30	**Break**
10:30–12:00	**Introduction** • Understand the ALCOA components • A look into the good documentation practice
12:00–13:00	**Lunch**

13:00–14:00	**Data Integrity Roles and Responsibilities**
14:00–14:30	**Inventory Management**
14:30–15:00	**Use of Spreadsheets** • Advantages • Disadvantages
15:00–15:15	**Break**
15:15–15:45	**Practice Exercise**
15:45–17:00	**Information Technology and Data Integrity** • What are electronic records? • ERES regulations • How the ALCOA is applied to electronic records • Computerized system validation—risk-based approach • End-user applications • Triggers for e-data integrity loss

Title: Data integrity certification (day 2)

Lunch: 12:00–13:00

Coffee Break: 15 minutes each during morning and afternoon session. Time schedules are rough estimates and may vary consequently.

Agenda	
8:30–10:15	**Introduction to Laboratory Perspective** • Specifications and standards • Sampling plans
10:15–10:30	**Break**
10:30–12:00	**Test Procedures** • Regulatory observations
12:00–13:00	**Lunch**

13:00–14:00	**Laboratory Controls** • 21CFR§ 211 requirement
14:00–15:15	**Laboratory Records** • Regulatory observations
15:15–16:00	**Break**
16:00–17:00	**Good Documentation Practices** • Analyst function • Formats for laboratory data collection • Types of laboratory documents

Title: Data integrity certification (day 3)

Lunch: 12:00–13:00

Coffee Break: 15 minutes each during morning and afternoon session. Time schedules are rough estimates and may vary consequently.

Agenda	
8:30–9:30	**Production and Process Controls**
9:30–10:15	**Facilities/Equipment**
10:15–10:30	**Break**
10:30–11:00	**Materials Management**
11:00–12:00	**Records** • Regulatory observations • Good documentation practices
12:00–13:00	**Lunch**
13:00–14:00	**Document Management** • Control • Retention

14:00–15:15	**Quality Unit Responsibilities**
15:15–15:30	**Break**
15:30–16:00	**Data Integrity Effort and Remediation** • Prevention • Detection • Remediation
16:00–16:30	**FDA Perspective on Data Integrity Remediation**
16:30–17:00	**Post-test**

Appendix C

Guidelines for Auditing ALCOA Principles for Paper and Electronic Documents

The following pages contain ALCOA auditing/assessment questions for both paper and electronic documents. A classification of good documentation practices/data integrity deficiencies based on the risk of the situation is included. It is important to have an overall picture of the adequacy of the key elements (data governance process, design of systems to facilitate compliant data recording, use and verification of audit trails, IT user access, and so on) to make a robust assessment as to whether there is a company-wide failure or a deficiency of limited scope/impact.

Individual circumstances (exacerbating/mitigating factors) may also affect final classification of the deficiency and in cases of regulatory inspection, as they might determine the kind of regulatory action to be taken by regulators.

CLASSIFICATION OF DEFICIENCIES

The following guidance is intended to aid consistency in reporting and classification of data integrity deficiencies. Deficiencies relating to data integrity failure may have varying impact on product quality. Prevalence of the failure may also vary between the action of a single employee to an endemic failure throughout the inspected organization.

A critical deficiency is a practice or process that has created or leads to a significant risk of producing a medical product that is harmful. A critical deficiency also occurs when it is observed that the manufacturer has engaged in fraud, misrepresentation, or falsification of products or data.

As an example, Health Canada considers that any findings involving fraud, misrepresentation, or falsification of products or data to be a risk 1 (critical) observation.[1] Some examples of this are as follows:

---

[1] Health Canada (2018). *Risk Classification Guide for Drug Good Manufacturing Practices Observations (GUI-0023)*.

- There was evidence that manufacturing and/or packaging orders were falsified or misrepresented

- Analytical samples, test results, or raw data were misrepresented or fabricated

- Deleted or destroyed records, results, or raw data were used to support release

Notwithstanding the "critical" classification of deficiencies relating to fraud, misrepresentation, or falsification, it is understood that data integrity deficiencies can also relate to:

- Data integrity failure resulting from bad practice

- Opportunity for failure (without evidence of actual failure) due to absence of the required data control measures

In these cases, it may be appropriate to assign classification of deficiencies by considering the following (indicative list only):

Impact to product with risk to patient health: Critical deficiency

- Product failing to meet specification at release or within shelf life

- Reporting of a "desired" result rather than an actual out-of-specification result when reporting QC tests, critical product, or process parameters

Impact to product with no risk to patient health: Major deficiency

- Data being misreported (for example, original results "in specification," but altered to give a more favorable trend)

- Reporting of a "desired" result rather than an actual out-of-specification result when reporting of data that does not relate to QC tests, critical product, or process parameters

- Failures arising from poorly designed data capture systems (for example, using scraps of paper to record info for later transcription)

No impact to product, evidence of widespread failure: Major deficiency

- Bad practices and poorly designed systems that may result in opportunities for data integrity issues or loss of traceability across several functional areas (QA, production, QC, and so on). Each on their own has no direct impact to product quality.

No impact to product, limited evidence of failure: Other deficiency

- Bad practice or poorly designed system that results in opportunities for data integrity issues or loss of traceability in a discrete area
- Limited failure in an otherwise acceptable system

PAPER RECORDS GAP ASSESSMENT

Attributable

- Does the document provide space to record the name/initials/signature, date, and, when necessary, time for the person performing the task, the review, or the approval?
- Are the people signing and dating the tasks, reviews, and approvals included in the site master signature list?
- Are signatures being permanently linked to the record being signed?
- Do the personnel working with this GMP system have the proper training?
- Is the information that allows attribution specifically requested as a result of the design of the record?
- Does the system print out GMP data that are part of the record (for example, checkweigher, chromatogram, and so on)?
- Does the system print out records information such as username, date, and time?
- Is the data printout uniquely identified as executed by the originator of the data?
- Is the access to change this information restricted to authorized individuals?
- Are record changes attributable?
- Are unused or invalidated spaces within the record attributable?
- Is a personal seal to sign documents used?

- Is there a procedure that requires storage of the seal in a secure location with access limited only to the assigned individual, or equipped with other means of preventing potential misuse? Is it being followed accordingly?

Legible

- Is the record designed to ensure there is sufficient space to record the GMP data elements and all pertinent metadata?
- Is the record filled in with indelible ink?
- If the "system" enables a printed form of GMP data, is the media durable for the lifetime of the record?
- Do system printouts include all the data and metadata?
- Are handwritten entries legible?
- Is scribbling or overwriting found?
- Is the issuance of sequentially numbered copies of blank forms controlled, allowing all issued forms to be accounted for?
- Is the issuance of bound paginated notebooks with sequentially numbered pages controlled, allowing detection of missing or skipped pages?
- Are single-line cross-outs properly documented, including name of the person making the cross-out, date, and reason for change?
- Is the archiving of paper records performed by independent, designated personnel in secure and controlled archives?

Contemporaneous

- Are there enough space and instructions to attached relevant process printouts to support the accuracy and contemporaneous recording of data?
- Does the design of the form encourage and require the recording of GMP data pertinent to each step in the process before moving to the next step?
- Is date and time included as a requirement to support contemporaneous recording and/or compliance with the process specifications?

- Are there written procedures and training for the review, audit, and self-inspection controls to ensure that personnel record the data entries and information at the time of the activity directly in official controlled documents (for example, laboratory notebooks, batch records, CRFs)?

- If the system provides a printout, do the printouts include the date stamp?

- Does the recording of the date and time of activities use synchronized time sources (facility and computerized system clocks) that cannot be changed by unauthorized personnel?

- If a spreadsheet is used for calculations, does the form have the controls for recording the date and time at the moment of the activity (for example, controlled printout timestamp)?

Original

- Is there a procedure and process that defines the requirements for the controlled issuance, reconciliation, and review of the record?

- Do the issuance, reconciliation, and control strategies prevent unauthorized copying or replacement of the GMP record?

- Is the "system" number and version controlled?

- For spreadsheets used for calculation purposes (where they do not control the original source GMP data), is the master version controlled and secured for unauthorized change?

  – Is it password protected?

  – Are there procedures that define how to save data and/or print the GMP record?

- Are the original data record and/or true copies preserving the content and meaning of the original data?

  – Is it retained?

- Are copies of the record being verified?

- Is there a procedure establishing the steps for creating and certifying a true copy of the record?

- Are the original data properly found within the record (for example, there are no data recorded in a temporary system memory)?

- Is there a procedure describing the actions to be taken if data review identifies an error or omission? This procedure should enable data corrections or clarifications to be made in a GMP-compliant manner, providing visibility of the original record and audit-trailed traceability of the correction, using ALCOA principles.

Accurate

- Does the system/document have a change control?
- Are changes to the form/record template governed by a change control?
- Is system usage properly recorded? (Maintenance record, cleaning record, preventive maintenance record, sampling record, and so on)
- Is the system qualified, validated, and calibrated as applicable?
- Are investigations of deviations and/or doubtful and/or out-of-specification results for the system performed following appropriate procedures?

ELECTRONIC RECORDS GAP ASSESSMENT

Attributable

- Are training records for the system users, supervisors, maintenance, and administrators available?
- Do the systems administrators have a user's list, including user roles and privileges, and is it updated and revised regularly?
- Does the system have requirements for electronic signatures?
- Is the electronic signature linked to a defined electronic record?
- Are the electronic signatures unique?
- Are the signatures securely and permanently linked to the record being signed?
- Do the audit trails capture user identification (ID) and date- and timestamps?
- Does the system have unique user logins that link the user to actions such as creating, modifying, or deleting data?

- Is there a defined period of inactivity resulting in system timeout/lockout?

- Are there defined user access levels for the application, database, and middleware?

- Have these access roles been tested during validation?

- Do the access roles include systems administration access for this GMP computerized system?

- Does each systems administrator have a unique individualized login?

  - If no, there must be an alternate method of providing traceability (date, time, actions). Provide reference to alternative methodology.

- Are systems administrator actions captured in the audit trail and are they attributed to the specific individual?

- Does the system prevent or detect unauthorized use of IDs and or passwords?

- Are there logical controls (for example, is there a procedure establishing the process to manage and control access levels, password, and so on)?

- Does the system validation documentation include devices or tokens that bear or generate ID or password information?

- Have these been tested to ensure they function as intended?

- Are they periodically retested using a risk-based approach to confirm they have not been altered in an unauthorized manner?

- Is there an established periodic review of system access?

- Is the personal access to the system commensurate with job responsibilities?

Legible

- Does the system's electronic records requirement include noneditable date- and timestamped audit trails?

- Are the system's audit trails related to GMP electronic records enabled?

- Do system requirements include prevention of audit trail disabling?

  – Has this function been tested?

- Do the system audit trail requirements include capturing identity of the user in entries and actions for creation, modification, or deletion of electronic records?

- Does the system design and function prevent overwriting or obscuring of previously recorded information?

- Do the configuration settings restrict the access to enhanced security permissions (such as the systems administrator role that can be used to potentially turn off the audit trails or enable overwriting and deletion of data), only to persons independent of those responsible for the content of the electronic records?

- Are there configuration settings and SOPs, as required, to disable and prohibit the ability to overwrite data, including prohibiting overwriting of preliminary and intermediate processing of data?

- Does the system have a strictly controlled configuration and use of data annotation tools in a manner that prevents data in displays and printouts from being obscured or hidden?

- Have the backups of electronic records been validated to ensure recovery?

- If the existing computerized system lacks computer-generated audit trails, are there alternative means such as procedurally controlled use of logbooks, change control, record version control, or other combinations of paper and electronic records to meet GXP regulatory expectations for traceability to document the what, who, when, and why of an action?

- Are the electronic records, archived manually or automatically, stored in secure and controlled electronic archives, accessible only by independent, designated archivists or by their approved delegates?

- Is there appropriate separation of duties established so business process owners, or other users who may have a conflict of interest, are not granted enhanced security access permissions at any system level (for example, operating system, application, and database)?

Contemporaneous

- Are signatures and personal seals executed at the time of review or performance of the event or action being recorded?

- Does the system validation include established controls to ensure data integrity elements such as data security, access roles/permissions, sequence of operations, enabling of relevant audit trail, and so on?

- Does the system ensure the execution of GMP operations is recorded contemporaneously by the user and is not combined with other operations?

- Is the system time and date synchronized with an official/certified source?

- Is the system date and time fixed in a way that unauthorized personnel are not allowed to change it?

- Are there configuration settings, procedures, and controls to ensure data recorded in temporary memory are committed to durable media upon completion of the step or event and before proceeding to the next step or event to ensure the permanent recording of the step or event at the time it is conducted?

- Are there procedures to ensure time/date stamps are synchronized and maintained as such across the GMP operations?

Original

- Does the validation include challenges to the system capability to prevent the electronic signature from being edited, deleted, copied, or transferred?

- Does the system generate accurate and complete copies of the electronic record (suitable for review and or copying to support regulatory inspections)?

- Do copies preserve the content and meaning in a human-readable format?

- Does the system printout indicate whether any of the GMP data have been changed since the original entry?

- Have the functions for generating copies been defined in system documentation (reporting requirements, report design, and functions)?

- Have these (reports, printouts) been validated?

- Are there operational procedures or instructions for generating these reports?

- Is the audit trail being viewed or copied in a format that is readable and has meaning?

- Does the audit trail capture GMP-relevant changes to the database, system-specific accounts, system privileges, and system roles?

- Are there system-specific procedures or instructions related to view/review of the audit trail?

- Are the audit trails included in the data/record backup?

- If it is an open system, are there additional security measures to ensure the integrity of data?

- Are electronic records, data, metadata, and corresponding audit trails protected from deliberate and inadvertent destruction or alteration?

- Does the system have the capability to ensure the records remain accessible, accurate, readable, and readily retrievable for the entire retention period?

- Are archived data periodically checked for accessibility, readability, and integrity?

- Are archived records secured so they cannot be altered or deleted without detection and an audit trail entry?

- Is the system validation and supporting documentation stored and secured in a controlled area?

- Are electronic records and data secured against loss and damage?

- Has backup and restoration services for the system (software and configuration) as well as system records/data been established?

- Do these align with the system risks and criticality of data?

- Did the system validation include verification of the integrity and accuracy of backup records/data?

- Did the system validation include verification of the ability to restore the data?

- Is the ability to restore the data periodically monitored?

- Are documented disaster recovery exercises conducted?

- Do disaster recovery exercises include integrity and accuracy of data, restoring data, and hardware/software?

- Are the designated data archivists (for example, IT department resources) qualified and do they have the relevant experience and appropriate training to perform their duties?

- Are there written procedures for training, review, audit, and inspection controls that ensure personnel can conduct an adequate review and approval of original electronic records, including human-readable source records of electronic records?

- Is there a procedure describing the actions to be taken if data review identifies an error or omission? This procedure should enable data corrections or clarifications to be made in a GMP-compliant manner, providing visibility of the original record and audit-trailed traceability of the correction, using ALCOA principles.

- Are the frequency, roles, and responsibilities, and the approach used to review the various types of meaningful metadata, such as audit trails, established?

- Are internal quality assurance audits (self-inspection) established and performed?

- Are routine backup copies of original electronic records stored in another location as a safeguard in case of disaster that causes loss of the original electronic records?

- Are storage areas, including archives, for electronic records controlled and secure?

- Is the ability to retrieve archived electronic data from the storage locations periodically tested, including retrieval from third-party storage?

- Are there written procedures for training, review, audit, and self-inspection of processes defining conversion, as needed, of original electronic records to true copy?

Accurate

- Did the validation include a risk management approach that considered GMP utilization and inclusion of electronic records?

- Has the GMP computerized system been validated following a validation life cycle methodology?

- Does the system function to prohibit the entry of invalid data or the ability to alter records?

- Are there operational checks (for example, all results entered and within specification before sample/lot release can occur)?

- Are there controls for external device connections?

- Has the system vendor/supplier/service provider been qualified?

- Is the equipment or system under appropriate maintenance program as applicable?

- If there's data transference from another system, is the data transfer between systems validated?

- Are there specific planned testing and controls for the migration of data to and from the system?

Bibliography

European Commission. 2011. EudraLex Volume 4: Good Manufacturing Practice Medicinal Products for Human and Veterinary Use. Annex 11: *Computerised Systems*.

European Medicines Agency (EMA). 2016. *Questions and Answers: Good Manufacturing Practice-Data Integrity*.

Food and Drug Administration (FDA). 1976. *Inspection Technical Guide 23: The Computer in FDA Regulated Industries*. Washington, DC: FDA.

———. 1978. 21 Code of Federal Regulations § Part 211—Current Good Manufacturing Practices for Finished Pharmaceuticals. Washington, DC: Federal Register.

———. 1983. *Guide to Inspection of Computerized Systems in Drug Establishments*. Washington, DC: FDA.

———. 1997. *21 CFR Part 11—Electronic Records; Electronic Signatures*. Washington, DC: FDA.

———. 2002. *Final Guidance for Industry and FDA Staff—General Principles of Software Validation*. Final Guidance for Industry and Staff. Washington, DC.

———. 2003. *Part 11, Electronic Records; Electronic Signatures—Scope and Application*. Guidance for Industry. Washington, DC.

———. 2007. *Guidance for Industry—Computerized Systems Used in Clinical Investigations*. Washington, DC: FDA.

———. 2018. *Guidance for Industry on Data Integrity and Compliance with cGMP*. Washington, DC: FDA.

Health Canada. 2018. *Risk Classification Guide for Drug Good Manufacturing Practices Observations (GUI-0023)*. Ottawa: Health Canada.

Hicks, Karen M. 1994. *Surviving the Dalcon Shield IUD: Women v. The Pharmaceutical Industry*. New York: Teachers College Press.

International Organization for Standardization (ISO). 2016. ISO 13485:2016 *Medical Devices—Quality Management Systems—Requirements for Regulatory Purposes*. Geneva: ISO.

International Society for Pharmaceutical Engineering (ISPE). 2008. *GAMP 5 Guide: A Risk-Based Approach to Compliant GxP Computerized Systems*. Tampa, FL: ISPE.

———. 2017. *Records and Data Integrity Guide*. Tampa, FL: ISPE.

Lopez, Orlando. 2017. *Data Integrity in Pharmaceutical and Medical Devices Regulation Operations*. Boca Raton, FL: CRC Press.

Parenteral Drug Association (PDA). 2018. *Technical Report No. 80: Data Integrity Management System for Pharmaceutical Laboratory*. Bethesda, MD: PDA.

Pharmaceutical Inspection Co-operation Scheme (PIC/S). 2018. Draft 3 *Guidance Good Practices for Data Management and Integrity in Regulated GMP/ GDP Environments*. Geneva: PIC/S.

Rattan, Anil. 2018. "Data Integrity: History, Issues, and Remediation of Issues." *PDA J Pharm Sci Technol* 72 (March/April 2018): 105–116.

Rodríguez-Pérez, José. 2017. *Quality Risk Management for the FDA-Regulated Industry*. 2nd Edition. Milwaukee, WI: ASQ Quality Press.

United Kingdom Medicines and Healthcare Product Regulatory Agency (MHRA). 2018. *GXP Data Integrity Definitions and Guidance*. London: MHRA.

World Health Organization (WHO). 2016. Annex 5: *Guidance on Good Data Management and Record Management Practices*. *WHO Technical Report Series, No. 996*. Geneva: WHO.

Web Pages

http://apps.who.int/medicinedocs/documents/s22402en/s22402en.PDF. Accessed December 26, 2018.

http://eudragmdp.ema.europa.eu/inspections/gmpc/searchGMPNonCompliance .do. Accessed December 29, 2018.

http://www.financialexpress.com/industry/european-union-bans-700-generic-drugs -for-manipulation-of-trials-by-gvk-biosciences/107418/. Accessed December 24, 2018.

http://www.ich.org/fileadmin/Public_Web_Site/ICH_Products/Guidelines /Efficacy/E6/E6_R2__Step_4_2016_1109.PDF. Accessed December 15, 2018.

https://assets.publishing.service.gov.uk/government/uploads/system/uploads /attachment_data/file/687246/MHRA_GxP_data_integrity_guide_March _edited_Final.PDF. Accessed December 28, 2018.

https://ec.europa.eu/health/documents/eudralex/vol-4_en. Accessed December 29, 2018.

https://extranet.who.int/prequal/content/notices-concernsuspension. Accessed December 27, 2018.

https://extranet.who.int/prequal/sites/default/files/documents/NOC_Semler 12April2016.PDF. Accessed December 27, 2018.

https://www.accessdata.fda.gov/cms_ia/importalert_189.html. Accessed December 27, 2018.

https://www.fda.gov/downloads/drugs/developmentapprovalprocess/manufactur ing/questionsandanswersoncurrentgoodmanufacturingpracticescgmpfordrugs /ucm071871.PDF. Accessed December 29, 2018.

https://www.fda.gov/downloads/Drugs/GuidanceComplianceRegulatoryInformation /EnforcementActivitiesbyFDA/UCM382514.PDF. Accessed December 27, 2018.

https://www.fda.gov/downloads/Drugs/GuidanceComplianceRegulatoryInformati on/Guidances/UCM080584.PDF. Accessed December 29, 2018.

https://www.fda.gov/downloads/drugs/guidances/ucm070287.pdf. Accessed December 29, 2018.

https://www.fda.gov/downloads/drugs/guidances/ucm495891.PDF. Accessed December 25, 2018.

https://www.fda.gov/downloads/RegulatoryInformation/Guidances/ucm125125 .PDF. Accessed December 29, 2018.

https://www.fda.gov/downloads/RegulatoryInformation/Guidances/UCM360484 .PDF. Accessed December 29, 2018.

https://www.fda.gov/Drugs/DrugSafety/ucm495778.htm. Accessed December 27, 2018.

https://www.fda.gov/ICECI/ComplianceManuals/CompliancePolicyGuidance-Manual/ucm073837.htm. Accessed December 26, 2018.

https://www.fda.gov/ICECI/EnforcementActions/ApplicationIntegrityPolicy /ucm134453.htm. Accessed December 26, 2018.

http://www.fda.gov/ICECI/EnforcementActions/ApplicationIntegrityPolicy /ucm134744.htm. Accessed December 29, 2018.

https://www.fda.gov/iceci/enforcementactions/fdadebarmentlist/default.htm. Accessed December 28, 2018.

https://www.fda.gov/ICECI/EnforcementActions/FDADebarmentList/ucm194263 .htm. Accessed December 28, 2018.

https://www.fda.gov/ICECI/EnforcementActions/ucm321308.htm. Accessed December 29, 2018.

https://www.fda.gov/iceci/enforcementactions/warningletters/2013/ucm369409 .htm. Accessed December 29, 2018.

https://www.fda.gov/ICECI/EnforcementActions/WarningLetters/2014 /ucm409898.htm. Accessed December 29, 2018.

https://www.fda.gov/ICECI/EnforcementActions/WarningLetters/2015 /ucm432709.htm. Accessed December 29, 2018.

https://www.fda.gov/ICECI/EnforcementActions/WarningLetters/2015 /ucm474013.htm. Accessed December 29, 2018.

https://www.fda.gov/ICECI/EnforcementActions/WarningLetters/2015 /ucm479712.htm. Accessed December 29, 2018.

https://www.fda.gov/iceci/enforcementactions/warningletters/2016/ucm489735 .htm. Accessed December 29, 2018.

https://www.fda.gov/iceci/enforcementactions/warningletters/2016/ucm508291 .htm. Accessed December 29, 2018.

https://www.fda.gov/iceci/enforcementactions/warningletters/2016/ucm518540 .htm. Accessed December 29, 2018.

https://www.fda.gov/ICECI/EnforcementActions/WarningLetters/2017 /ucm546483.htm. Accessed December 29, 2018.

https://www.fda.gov/ICECI/EnforcementActions/WarningLetters/default.htm. Accessed December 29, 2018.

https://www.fda.gov/ICECI/EnforcementActions/WarningLetters/ucm361553
.htm. Accessed December 27, 2018.

https://www.fda.gov/ICECI/EnforcementActions/WarningLetters/ucm409898
.htm. Accessed December 29, 2018.

https://www.fda.gov/ICECI/EnforcementActions/WarningLetters/ucm480035
.htm. Accessed December 29, 2018.

https://www.fda.gov/ICECI/EnforcementActions/WarningLetters/ucm608713
.htm. Accessed December 29, 2018.

https://www.fda.gov/RegulatoryInformation/LawsEnforcedbyFDA/Significant
AmendmentstotheFDCAct/FDASIA/default.htm. Accessed December 29, 2018.

https://www.fdli.org/2018/04/update-fda-data-integrity-enforcement-trends
-practical-mitigation-measures/. Accessed December 29, 2018.

https://www.justice.gov/opa/pr/generic-drug-manufacturer-ranbaxy-pleads-guilty
-and-agrees-pay-500-million-resolve-false. Accessed December 27, 2018.

https://www.nytimes.com/1976/04/08/archives/fda-urges-grand-jury-study-of-gd
-searles-drug-reports.html. Accessed December 24, 2018.

https://www.picscheme.org/layout/document.php?id=149. Accessed December 28,
2018.

http://www.picscheme.org/layout/document.php?id=1566. Accessed December 18,
2018.

https://www.raps.org/regulatory-focus%E2%84%A2/news-articles/2015/2/india-s
-data-integrity-problems. Accessed December 27, 2018.

Index

Note: Page numbers followed by *t* refer to tables.

A

Able Laboratories, 188
accuracy criteria, 12, 57–58, 57*t*, 68*t*,
    75*t*, 78*t*, 226, 231–232
Actavis Totowa, 194–195
AIP (application integrity policies),
    62, 83, 87, 154
ALCOA (attributable, legible, con-
    temporaneous, original, and
    accurate) principles
    accurate, 12, 57–58, 57*t*, 68*t*, 75*t*,
        78*t*, 226, 231–232
    attributable, 11, 37–40, 38*t*, 68*t*,
        75*t*, 78*t*, 177, 223–224, 226–227
    clinical data integrity with, 124
    contemporaneous, 11, 28, 44, 45*t*,
        68*t*, 75*t*, 78*t*, 224–225, 229
    data defined in relation to, 8
    data review, reporting, and
        approval based on, 98
    deficiencies in, classification of,
        221–223
    defined, 6, 8, 11–12
    expectations and examples of,
        37–58
    good documentation practices and,
        11–12, 37
    guidelines for auditing, 221–232
    legible, traceable, and permanent,
        11, 40–43, 41*t*–42*t*, 68*t*, 75*t*,
        78*t*, 224, 227–228

original, 12, 46–57, 48*t*–49*t*,
    52*t*–54*t*, 68*t*, 75*t*, 78*t*, 225–226,
    229–231
quality management system includ-
    ing, 57–58, 57*t*, 103
regulatory expectations for, 2, 4,
    67, 68*t*, 74, 75*t*, 77, 78*t*–79*t*
risk management considerations
    for, 37–58
ALCOA+ (complete, consistent,
    enduring, and available)
    principles
    available, 12, 79*t*
    complete, 12, 79*t*
    consistent, 12, 79*t*
    data defined in relation to, 8
    defined, 6, 12
    enduring, 12, 79*t*
    good documentation practices and,
        11–12
    regulatory expectations for, 77,
        78*t*–79*t*
Alkem Laboratories, 214
application integrity policies (AIP),
    62, 83, 87, 154
archives
    ALCOA principles on, 41*t*–42*t*, 43,
        51, 52*t*–53*t*, 54, 224, 228, 231
    data life cycle including, 100–102
    data transfer and migration of,
        100–101, 168–169
    defined, 7

WHY ASQ?

ASQ is a global community of people passionate about quality, who use the tools,
their ideas and expertise to make our world work better. ASQ: The Global Voice of Quality.

OR INDIVIDUALS

vance your career to the next level of excellence.

SQ offers you access to the tools, techniques and insights that can help distinguish
ordinary career from an extraordinary one.

OR ORGANIZATIONS

ur culture of quality begins here.

SQ organizational membership provides the invaluable resources you need
concentrate on product, service and experiential quality and continuous
provement for powerful top-line and bottom-line results.

www.asq.org/why-asq

ASQ
The Global Voice of Quality

ASK A LIBRARIAN

Have questions? Looking for answers? In need of information? Ask a librarian!

Customized research assistance from ASQ's research librarian is one of the many benefits of membership. ASQ's research librarian is available to answer your research requests using the everexpanding library of current and credible resources, including journals, conference proceedings, case studies, and Quality Press publications.

You can also contact the librarian to request permission to reuse or reprint ASQ copyrighted material, such as ASQ journal articles and Quality Press book excerpts.

For more information or to submit a question, visit asq.org/quality-resources/ask-a-librarian.

ASQ
The Global Voice of Quality